The Legend of The Lost Keys

Jim Eldridge

D0487389

LOOK and Read

BBC

Published by BBC Educational Publishing,
201 Wood Lane, London W12 7TS

First published 1997

© Jim Eldridge/BBC Worldwide (Educational Publishing)

The moral right of the author has been asserted.

Illustrations © Peter Ware 1997

ISBN 0 563 46048 2

Set in Stone Informal 10 point

Printed and bound in Great Britain by Clays Ltd, St Ives plc

CONTENTS

1 THE BOX   5

2 THE FIRST KEY   22

3 THE WATCHERS   30

4 KIDNAP   38

5 THE CRYSTAL CONNECTION   52

6 THE TRAP   64

7 THE BOX IS OPENED   74

8 INTO THE BOX   89

9 BETRAYED   104

10 THE FINAL HOUR   115

The Legend of The Lost Keys

If the Box of Destiny is ever found
Then whosoever finds the three keys
Can lock the doorway open
Or lock the doorway shut.
But above all, they must have the two
Children of Heritron
Then the fate of Heritron will be sealed
For ever.

'HERE we are,' said Uncle George. 'Welcome back to Guardian's Green!'

He pulled up outside the old house in the centre of the park. The rear doors of his car opened and Mark and Lisa got out and looked around. They had been coming to Guardian's Green to stay for a week every summer for as long as they could remember. Every time they came, it looked the same: beautiful trees, shrubs and flowers; a haven of peace in the middle of the busy town. They usually came with their mother, but this year, for the first time, they were on their own. Their mother had gone to look after their grandfather, who had just come out of hospital after an operation.

'Come on!' said George.

They hurried into the house, where they were greeted by a young woman in working clothes.

'You remember Erica?' asked George.

Mark nodded and shook Erica's hand.

'You were here last year,' he said.

'That's right,' smiled Erica. 'I'd just started working in the park when you came last summer.' To George she added: 'I've made lunch.'

'Great!' said Mark. 'I'm starving after that journey.'

They were just about to settle down to eat, when there was a loud knock at the front door.

'Who on earth could that be?' asked George. He opened the door, and the two children saw the expression on his face turn grim. Three people were on the doorstep: a very well-dressed man at the front, and a man and a woman behind him.

'Mr Gardner,' said the well-dressed man, curtly.

'Well, well, Sir Derek Janus again,' said George. 'And to what do we owe the pleasure this time, Sir Derek? As if I couldn't guess.'

Janus produced a sheet of paper with a wax seal on it.

'I have here a court order that allows us access to the park for the purpose of recovering important Roman remains,' he said.

'What court order?' demanded George. 'I wasn't notified of this! My solicitors have told me . . .'

'Your solicitors have today conceded defeat,' interrupted Janus. 'This court order was issued this morning and there's nothing you can do about it.'

'We'll see about that,' snorted George. 'Court order or no court order, I'm not having a bunch of vandals invade my property!'

'Vandals!' retorted Janus. 'This is Professor Humphrey Waters, the country's leading expert on Roman archaeology, and his assistant, Dr Stephanie Burns.'

'What's going on, Uncle George?' asked Mark.

'We are looking for a Roman box of enormous significance that we believe was hidden somewhere in this area,' explained Professor Waters. 'We know there's an ancient pavilion in this park and it is my belief that the box may be hidden there.'

'This park is private property,' stated George firmly.

'Maybe, but it's not exempt from the law,' said Janus just as firmly, and he waved the court order at George.

'I'll see what the police have to say about this,' snapped George.

He turned and stormed into the house. Janus, Waters and Burns moved off to begin their search for the old pavilion and the box. Lisa and Mark exchanged concerned looks.

'Poor Uncle George,' sighed Lisa.

They both turned to Erica.

'Has this been going on for long?' they asked.

'Months,' answered Erica. 'So far it's just been argued in court, but now it looks as if the hunt begins.'

'Well, I'm going to keep an eye on that lot,' said Mark. 'Make sure they don't damage anything.'

'I'll come with you,' nodded Erica.

'I'll stay with Uncle George,' said Lisa, 'to see how he gets on with the police.'

Mark and Erica hurried off after Janus, Waters and Burns, while Lisa went into the kitchen.

George was already on the phone to his solicitors as Lisa came in.

'You mean these people can just burst in here . . . on private property . . . and . . .' he said angrily. He listened a little more, then slammed down the receiver.

'No luck, Uncle George?' asked Lisa.

'Apparently there's some law that relates to an ancient treasure trove,' said George unhappily.

Just then Mark rushed in.

'Uncle George, they're talking about breaking into the old building!' said Mark.

'What!' shouted George, alarmed.

Outside in the park, Janus, Waters and Burns had cleared most of the ivy from an old building. Mark and Lisa could see that it really was very old, the stones marked with holes from years and years of weather and ivy. The ancient iron gates stood firmly locked.

'Don't you touch that building!' shouted George. 'I don't care if you think you've got the law on your side or not! That building is ancient!'

'It certainly is!' cried Waters excitedly. 'It's Roman! I recognised the markings on it!'

'And it's where the box will be,' Janus added.

Waters turned to George: 'Do you have a key?'

'No, I don't!' George replied.

Janus moved over to the gates and placed his fingers against the lock. There was a movement and a low sound, and then the gate swung open.

'It seems to be unlocked after all,' said Janus.

He turned to George. Mark and Lisa noticed that the two men glared at each other, as if they both shared a terrible secret that no one else knew. George's face looked grim. He turned and left the old building. The children and Erica followed him.

'What's happening, Uncle George?' asked Mark.

'I've got to go out,' said George. 'I want you two to stay here with Erica. Is that alright, Erica?'

'Of course,' Erica nodded.

'Where are you going?' asked Lisa.

'To see someone,' said George.

'To get help?'

'Maybe,' said George.

With that he headed into the house. Mark and Lisa looked at each other, puzzled. What was Uncle George up to?

Waters and Burns hurried into the dusty and cobwebbed interior of the building and began clearing the dust and dirt from the floor, revealing the worn flagstones beneath.

'It must be here!' said Janus excitedly.

He and Waters began tapping the flagstones, listening to the sounds. With each one there was a dull, dead tone, telling them that there was just solid earth below. Then Waters tapped a flagstone, and it rang with a hollow sound.

'This is it!' he exclaimed. Waters and Janus lifted the stone and an ancient stairway was revealed. Waters switched on his torch and slowly descended the steps. Janus and Burns followed him into the darkness. It was pitch black, but suddenly the beam of the torch fell upon the shape of a small box.

'At last!' cried Professor Waters. 'I've found it!'

In his study, George opened a cupboard and took out a book of very old rolls of parchment. He slipped these inside his coat pocket. Returning outside the house, he called Mark and Lisa over to him.

'While I'm away, don't go near Janus and Waters,' he said. 'Let them get on with whatever they want. Don't interfere. Stay safe. Is that clear?'

Mark and Lisa nodded. Something terrible was happening, they could feel it.

'I'll be back as soon as I can,' said George.

George made his way to the busy main street of the town. He looked behind to make sure that he wasn't being followed and then slipped into a small alley, a dead-end, and headed for a derelict shop. The windows of the shop were covered in dust and grime, and the doors had long been locked. He checked again

to make sure that no one was watching, and then he opened the door and went inside.

Inside the shop there was dust everywhere. The wood was rotting. George went to the back of the shop where there was another door. He opened it and came face to face with a weird haze, like dimly glowing smoke.

Inside the haze, George found himself in a Crystal Capsule that seemed to go on for ever, with shelf after shelf of books going off in all directions, like a hall of mirrors.

A young woman looked up from the book that she was studying. She smiled at George.

'Salutations, Ariana,' George greeted her. 'Where is the Countess Anna? I must speak to her.'

Just then Anna appeared, a tall graceful woman, carrying a pile of books.

'George!' she cried in greeting. Then she saw the grim look on his face. 'What is wrong?'

'It has begun,' George replied. 'The Box of Destiny has been found.'

The Countess was clearly shocked.

'How did this happen?' she cried.

George continued: 'Sir Derek Janus, the man who's been so insistent about searching the park, is one of them! He's from Heritron! I saw him use his powers to open the doors of the old pavilion.'

'So it begins . . . as it was foretold,' Anna sighed. 'The final struggle has started.'

George took out the rolls of parchment from his pocket, laid them on the table and unrolled them. 'I've brought *The Book of the Guardian* with me. Now the Box of Destiny has been found, we will need it.'

'What are these?' asked Ariana, examining the parchments.

'These are *The Book of the Guardian*, written when the first Guardian hid the box nearly two thousand years ago,' said Anna. 'It has been guarded down the ages by every Guardian who followed.'

'How will it help us?' asked Ariana.

'It's a book of poems, written to help us in our quest to solve *The Legend of the Lost Keys*,' said George.

He carefully opened *The Book of the Guardian* and turned to the first poem.

'The first part of this first poem is the legend itself,' he said, and he began to read:

> 'If the Box of Destiny is ever found
> Then whosoever finds the three keys
> Can lock the doorway open
> Or lock the doorway shut.
> But above all, they must have the two Children
> of Heritron
> Then the fate of Heritron will be sealed
> For ever.'

Ariana looked confused.

'It was written in the old books that the tunnel between our world of Heritron and this world would one day be opened again,' Anna explained to her. 'The Box of Destiny, Ariana, is the doorway to the tunnel.'

'Where are the keys?' asked Ariana.

'No one knows,' said George. 'They were hidden by the Guardian when he hid the box. Now they are lost.'

'But above all, they must have the two Children of Heritron,' mused Anna, reading the scroll. 'I wonder who they are?'

'Well, the poem carries on,' said George:

>*'Who is the boy and who is the girl*
>*Who are the Children of Heritron?*
>*His name is in bark*
>*but not in bite*
>*With one thousand before.*
>*His friend in the fight*
>*Is his twin*
>
>*Life*
>*Is*
>*Serious*
>*Always.'*

They studied the poem for the next hour or so, then Ariana said: 'I think I have one of the names: Lisa!'

'What?' said George, shocked. 'How?'

'Take the first letter of each line. Life Is Serious Always. L . . . I . . . S . . . A. Lisa.'

'I have a thought about the boy's name,' said Anna. 'His name is in bark but not in bite. The letter B is in both. Remove "B" from bark, and you are left with "ark". So it could be Clark, or Mark.'

'That's astonishing!' said George, a stunned expression on his face.

'Why?' asked Anna.

'Because my niece and nephew who are staying with me at the moment are called Mark and Lisa. Does it mean they are the Children of Heritron?'

'It cannot be,' pointed out Ariana. 'They're from this world. Earth.'

'Yes, but they're my family,' explained George. 'And, like me, Mark and Lisa are descended from the original Guardian. Remember, he stayed behind after he'd locked the doorway.'

'It could be. But we must be absolutely certain!' exclaimed Anna. 'There is this other clue: "one thousand before".'

Anna took a book off the shelf and flicked over the pages, then beamed, satisfied.

'I thought so,' she said. 'The Guardian hid the box nearly two thousand years ago, during the time of Roman Britain. He was using Roman numbers. In Roman numbers, a thousand is "M". So "one thousand

before" means putting "M" before the word "ark". We were right. The poem means Mark and Lisa. They are the Children of Heritron. They are the ones who will find the keys to the box!'

'But how?' asked George, baffled.

Anna sighed. 'I do not know, but the legend cannot be wrong.'

By the time George got back to the park, the box had gone.

'They took it,' said Mark. 'They loaded it into their van. That Professor Waters said he was taking it to his workshop.'

George nodded glumly and then looked at Mark and Lisa sternly. 'Children, I need to talk to you.'

Inside his study, George paced around while Mark and Lisa stood and watched him. The twins exchanged puzzled looks behind his back. Uncle George was obviously deeply worried. Finally, he turned to them and said: 'You two are going to find what I'm about to tell you a bit hard to believe, but that box is more than just a box. It is the Box of Destiny, a doorway into another world. A world called Heritron.'

Mark and Lisa gaped at him. George continued: 'That box was locked shut and hidden here beneath the ground almost two thousand years ago by someone known as the Guardian. To make sure it would never be found, he hid it beneath that building, and then made this park around it. Since then, with every generation of his descendants, someone has taken over the job as Guardian. The Guardian's job has been to make sure the box stays safely hidden, so it can't be opened.'

'What would happen if the box is opened?' asked Lisa.

'That's something I hope you never have to see. If the box is opened, then the people from Heritron will come through and no child on this world will be safe. I am the latest Guardian.'

'Who . . . who are these other people? From this other world?' asked Lisa.

'They're called the Takers. And that's what they do: take. The Takers' world, Heritron, depends on – well, I suppose you'd call it technology. To support the way they live, they need slaves to work their machines. Lots of slaves. To get them, they take children from other worlds. They send people called Catchers to get these children and bring them back to Heritron.'

Mark and Lisa sat spellbound but horrified. George sighed, then carried on.

'After the box was sealed shut and hidden away, some of the Takers were left behind. These people were known as the Watchers. They made preparations for when the doorway could next be opened. Selected suitable children as slaves. That sort of thing.'

'But surely these Watchers who were left behind must have died out hundreds of years ago!' protested Lisa.

'They did,' replied George. 'But they had children. And their children had children, and so on. And their orders were still the same: "Find the Box of Destiny. Open the doorway. Bring us slaves." That man, Sir Derek Janus, is one.'

'Are you sure this isn't one of your stories, Uncle George?' asked Mark suspiciously.

'I wish it were,' sighed George.

'So, if the box was buried to stop it being opened, now that it's been dug up, Professor Waters will open it and these . . . Catchers . . . will come through,' said Lisa, horrified at the thought.

'Fortunately, it's not that easy,' explained George. 'The box is made of an indestructible material; at least, indestructible by anyone or anything in this world. There's only one way to open it, and that's with three keys, which the original Guardian hid after he locked the box.'

'Hid them where?' asked Lisa.

'No one actually knows,' said George. 'The secret died with him.'

'But if these keys don't turn up . . .' began Mark.

'Oh, they will, now that the box has been found,' said George grimly. 'The clues to the shape of the keys are given by the markings on the box. What we've got to do is make sure that we're the ones who find them.'

'I can't remember what any of the shapes on the lid looked like,' said Lisa.

'Nor can I,' said Mark.

'Then let's go and take a look,' suggested George. 'I'll get a camera and we'll go and take photos of them.'

'I don't think Professsor Waters will let you anywhere near it now he's got it,' said Mark ruefully.

'You may be right, Mark,' agreed George. He smiled. 'So I suggest we go when the Professor isn't around.'

2
THE FIRST KEY

THAT night, George, Mark and Lisa made their way to Professor Waters' workshop. George somehow managed to open a window. Mark frowned. He was convinced it had been locked. George helped Mark and Lisa climb in, and then he followed. They crept along the darkened corridors until they found the room with the box. George was just taking photographs of the lid, when all of a sudden the lights went on.

George turned. Waters and Burns were standing there. Professor Waters was looking grim.

'Well, Gardner!' he snapped. 'Caught red-handed. Like a thief in the night.'

'It's my box,' defended George. 'I'm entitled to look at it.'

'Your box?' queried Waters.

'I suppose you could call it an old family heirloom,' smiled George.

'And I suppose the police will call this breaking and entering. Which won't look good for these children, will it?' Waters sneered.

'You're only upset because you can't open the box,' said Mark in rather a scornful tone. 'Well, my Great Uncle knows how to open it.'

'That's enough, Mark!' said George sharply.

For the first time, the woman spoke.

'Do we really have to bring in the police, Professor?

After all, they're only children. And it could be bad publicity. Can you imagine if the papers got hold of it? The Janus Foundation wouldn't be too pleased.'

This stopped Waters in his tracks.

'Yes, you may have a point,' he admitted. Then he stared at George. 'Alright, but this is your last chance. If I see you or these children around here again, I will call in the police, publicity or no publicity.'

'Oh, you'll see me again, Professor,' said George defiantly. 'Whether you believe me or not, that box belongs to me and . . .'

Lisa tugged at George's arm.

'Please, Uncle George,' she whispered.

George hesitated, then followed the children outside to the street, where he held up the camera and grinned.

'At least we got what we came for.'

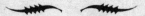

Inside the workshop, Professor Waters was tapping the box. It was true what that boy had said: he couldn't work out how to open it!

Dr Burns interrupted his examination of the box.

'Professor,' she said thoughtfully, 'that man obviously knows something about the box. And it was on his land. Maybe he does know something that could help us – *you* – open it. When we came in, he was taking photographs of these inscriptions. If we keep an eye on him, find out what he does with the photos . . .'

'. . . he might lead us to the keys to open it!' finished Waters. 'Yes! Well done, Burns! That could be the answer!'

Early next morning, George told Mark and Lisa that he had to go out again.

'About the box?' asked Mark.

'Yes,' nodded George.

'Excellent!' said Mark. 'We'll come with you!'

George shook his head. 'I'm sorry, you can't come where I'm going, but I'll tell you what you can do.'

He held out some of the photographs that they had taken of the box the night before.

'I want you to go and check these markings in the Roman section of the library. See what you can find out about them: what they represent, that sort of thing. It might give us a clue as to which ones are the keys.'

'You said you didn't want to leave us on our own,' said Mark accusingly, still hoping to persuade George to take them with him.

'I won't,' said George. 'I'll ask Erica if she'll do me a favour and go with you. It'll give her a break from working in the park. Only, don't tell Erica the real reason you're looking them up. We don't want her thinking we're cranks. Say it's for a school project.'
He looked at the sullen Mark. 'Is that okay with you?'

It wasn't okay with Mark. At the library he sat and watched Lisa and Erica going through books on Roman designs. He thought this was a con on Uncle George's part. In Mark's opinion, Uncle George had just given them this job to keep them away from where the real action was taking place. He bet that he was doing far more exciting things. Breaking into Professor Waters' place. Getting dynamite to blow up the box. Being chased by people. And what were he and Lisa doing? Sitting in a place surrounded by books! Huh!

In fact, it was exactly the same for George, because he was back with Anna and Ariana in the Crystal Capsule inside the old shop. They'd just worked out the meaning of the next poem-riddle. They'd worked out that the Guardian had hidden the first key, which was in the shape of an X, at a major crossroads that had existed in the town in Roman times.

As soon as George got back to the house, he collected Mark and Lisa and set off in the car.

'Where are we going?' asked Lisa.

'To a museum. The first key was buried at what used to be the Roman crossroads in the centre of the town. The site was dug up some time ago, but the Roman remains that were uncovered were put into a nearby museum. I'm hoping the key will still be on display there. It looks like this.' He handed them the photograph of the X-shaped design.

'How did you find this out?' asked Lisa.

'It's a long story. I'll tell you later,' said George.

'Huh! That's what adults always say,' thought Mark in annoyance.

As they drove, they didn't notice that they were being followed by Professor Waters and Dr Burns in Waters' car.

George parked in the museum car park, and they went in.

Inside the museum, they examined the exhibits in the glass cases, especially those marked 'Crossroads Excavation'. Lisa pointed excitedly at a photo on the wall. It was the photo of the key! But the key itself was not in the glass case.

'So, where is it?' asked Mark helplessly.

'That's what we're going to find out,' said George.

He hurried over to ask the nearest attendant.

The attendant sighed sadly.

'I'm afraid that piece was stolen months ago, along with some other pieces from the same section. That was before we put them under glass.'

'Terrible,' murmured George. 'Anyway, thank you for your time.'

With that, George gestured to Mark and Lisa, and the three hurried out of the museum. They didn't spot Waters and Burns, who had just arrived in the Roman Room. Waters saw George and the two children hurrying out at speed. His eyes narrowed suspiciously. What had they been up to?

Burns gave a little gasp.

'Professor Waters,' she whispered, pointing to the photo of the X on the wall. 'Isn't that like one of the designs on the box?'

Waters looked.

'It is!' he said excitedly. 'It's one of the keys! It must be here!'

He hurried to the display case, but, like George and the children, he found no sign of it.

'It isn't here now,' said Burns grimly. 'He must have stolen it!'

At the house, George and the two children were talking about the missing key.

'I reckon it was those others who stole it,' said Mark. 'The Watchers, whatever they're called.'

'Unlikely. That box was only discovered the other day. The attendant said that the piece went missing months ago, long before the Watchers would have known what they were looking for,' pointed out George. 'No, I think someone took it as a souvenir or to sell it. Tomorrow we'll start looking in all the second-hand and antique markets. If we're lucky, we might find it.'

That night, Lisa was asleep in her bed when a faint noise woke her up. Then she heard another noise. Someone was moving about downstairs!

She pulled on her dressing gown and went to wake up Mark

'Burglars!' he cried, still half asleep

'Sh!' warned Lisa.

They crept to the bannisters and looked over, and both nearly shouted out loud with shock. They could see two figures both dressed in black from head to foot. They were turning this way and that, listening and searching. Then their eyes turned upwards, and they saw Mark and Lisa. As the two children gasped in fear, the terrifying figures began to come up the stairs towards them!

Chapter 3

THE WATCHERS

THE two black-clothed figures suddenly tripped and tumbled back down the stairs. Mark and Lisa saw that George was behind the figures and had grabbed them by their ankles. The figures turned on George and were just about to attack him, when coats and hats, newspapers and letters seemed to lift up by themselves and started flying at them. They covered their heads against the objects, and made a rush for the door, fleeing out into the night.

Mark and Lisa stared down at the wreckage, astonished. What had happened?

Mark sprang into action.

'I'm going to phone the police!' he said, heading down the stairs.

'In normal circumstances, I would agree,' said George, stopping him. 'But not in this case. I'm afraid the police won't be much use.'

'Why?' demanded Mark. 'Who were those people?'

'And why did those things suddenly start to fly about?' asked Lisa.

George patted them both on the shoulders.

'I think this is a good time to go downstairs and have a cup of tea,' he said. 'And, while we drink it, I guess it's about time I told you the whole story.'

In the kitchen, as they drank their cups of tea, George explained: 'Those people were Watchers. They were looking for the keys to the box. If they find them before we do, then, as I said, a terrible fate will befall this world. They can only be stopped by two children. And, according to the poems, those two children are you.'

'The poems?' queried Mark.

'When the first Guardian hid the box, he wrote a series of secret poems to help future Guardians should the box ever be found. These ten poems form *The Book of the Guardian*. They will help us in our quest. The first poem actually mentions you by name.'

'By name?' gaped Mark. 'Mark and Lisa?'

George nodded.

'And he wrote this nearly two thousand years ago?' pressed Lisa.

Again, George nodded.

'Wow! This is . . . weird!' gasped Mark.

'To be honest, I had my doubts,' admitted George. And then he added: 'Until tonight. I didn't make those things fly around: you two did. The ones who are chosen as the Guardians have the power, to a degree.'

'What's the power?' asked Lisa.

'It's called telekinesis,' explained George. 'Using your mind to move something.' He smiled when he noticed the expression of disbelief on Mark's face. 'You don't believe it, Mark?'

Mark shook his head.

'I'm sorry, Uncle George, but this is all too . . . odd. It's the sort of thing you see in films,' he scoffed. 'Mind power!'

'Just because you can't see something, doesn't mean it doesn't exist,' said George. 'Take electricity, for example. You can't see it, but it's a real force. Yet a couple of hundred years ago, the idea that you pressed a switch and light came on would have been thought to be magic. And as for talking about the phone, or satellite communications, or the Internet – well, you'd have been burnt as a witch.'

'Yes, but this . . . !' protested Mark.

'It's only connecting to natural energy that's already there,' continued George. 'Like dowsing. You must have seen them on TV: these people who use a twig or a piece of metal to find water underground. Years ago it was thought to be supernatural. Now almost every water and electricity company in the world uses it.'

'Okay, say it did happen,' said Mark reluctantly. 'How do you know it was us who did it?'

'Well, it wasn't me, and those two would hardly have done it to themselves,' replied George, with a smile.

Mark and Lisa nodded. That was true.

'It's very late,' George said. 'I think you'd both better get to bed. Tomorrow we can get back on the track of the missing keys, and put your powers to good use.'

'Will those . . . Watchers . . . come back again?' asked Mark.

'Not tonight,' George reassured him. 'But, if you're worried . . .'

'Oh, I'm not worried!' grinned Mark. 'Not now I know I've got the power!'

'You may have it, but you can't control it – yet. If they come back, let me deal with them,' warned George. 'For one thing, if the Watchers discover what you two can do, they'll know that you two are the children – the Children of Heritron – referred to in the legend, and you'll be in very serious danger.'

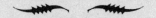

The next day, George Mark and Lisa went round all the antique and second-hand markets they could think of, but by the middle of the afternoon they still hadn't found the key. They decided to take a break in a café.

'This is useless!' groaned Mark. 'We must have tried every antique shop and junk shop in this town.'

Lisa noticed that George was holding a crystal in his hand, turning it over and over like a worry-stone.

'What's that?' she asked.

'It helps me concentrate,' said George. 'Here.'

Lisa took the crystal and held it in her hand, and, to her surprise, she was sure she could see it glowing deep inside.

'Kingston Market,' she muttered.

Mark looked at her, puzzled.

'Where?' he asked.

'Kingston Antique Market,' repeated Lisa. 'We haven't looked there yet.'

'But . . . you've never been to this Kingston Antique Market, have you?' asked Mark, more puzzled than ever.

'No. It just sort of popped into my head,' said Lisa. She felt puzzled about it, too. What had made her think of the place? She offered the crystal back to George, but he merely smiled and suggested that she hang on to it.

At Kingston Market they walked among the many different stalls. The crystal felt warm and friendly in Lisa's hand. She stopped by one of the stalls where she noticed a wooden box filled with all sorts of junk. She began to rummage around in it, turning over old coins and other bits and pieces. Then she held up a curious old piece of metal. It was the missing key!

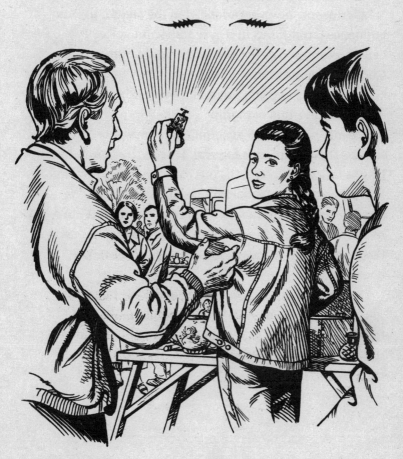

Inside the large forbidding building that housed the Janus Foundation, Sir Derek Janus was standing before a holographic communicator. The figure who looked out at Janus from the hologram was terrifying, with a hard and evil stare. This was the Supreme Taker.

'What news of the keys?' demanded the Taker.

'Our people have been following the Guardian, Your Eminence,' said Janus in a very respectful voice. 'I believe that some of the keys are already in the Guardian's possession.'

'Then why have you not taken them from him?' demanded the Taker, angrily.

'We are about to do just that, Your Eminence,' said Janus. 'The Guardian is forceful. He has the power. But he has one weak point. His niece and nephew, Lisa and Mark Astor, are staying with him at the moment. We are going to kidnap the two children. We will offer to release them in exchange for the Guardian giving us the keys! Within a very short time, we will have the doorway open!'

'See that you do,' growled the Taker. 'We have just seven days. Seven days before our machines begin to fail and Heritron faces certain collapse. We need more slaves to work the machines, Janus! We must have more slaves!'

CHAPTER 4   KIDNAP

MARK was angry. George had gone off again without telling him or Lisa where he was going. Mark was determined to find out what was going on. He crept into George's study and started rummaging through the papers on George's desk, looking for clues. As he stepped back from the desk, he accidentally knocked into a crystal mobile. Before Mark could grab it, the mobile crashed onto the floor. Mark looked down in horror. The mobile lay there, broken!

The sound of the crash brought Lisa and Erica running in and they looked at the broken mobile, shocked.

Just then Uncle George came back.

'Hello!' he began cheerfully. Then he stopped and stared at the mobile on the floor.

'The window was open and a gust of wind must have blown in and knocked that thing down,' lied Erica. 'We all heard this crashing sound and rushed in.'

George looked over at Mark, who turned away, looking guilty.

'I'll clear it up,' offered Erica, moving into the study.

'No, that's alright,' said George quickly. 'I'll do it later. Thanks, Erica.'

Erica went back to work, with a sympathetic smile at Mark and Lisa. Mark still looked miserable.

Once Erica had gone, George turned to Mark.

'How did that mobile really get broken?' he asked. 'There's no gust of wind that could have blown it down. And I know that window was shut because after those burglars the other night, I checked it before I went out.'

'I did it,' admitted Mark. 'It wasn't Erica's fault. She was protecting me. She wasn't even in here. Nor was Lisa. I wanted to find out what was going on. You keep going off and you don't tell us where.'

'That's true,' said George. 'And I'm sorry. I should have told you both sooner where I kept disappearing to, but I was worried because it affected other people. But it's time I told you about them.'

'Who?' asked Mark.

'One of them is the Countess Anna. The other is her daughter, Ariana. They're both from Heritron.'

Mark and Lisa looked baffled.

'How?' Mark asked. 'You said that box was the only link.'

'For the Takers it is, but Anna is the leader of the rebels on Heritron,' explained George. 'They want to change the way things are on Heritron: end slavery, let everyone have a fairer life. Anna developed something called a Crystal Capsule for travelling from world to world. Like the doorway, it can only be used when the two worlds are close together, and Anna used it to come here because she knew she was about to be imprisoned and all the knowledge she'd collected in the Crystal Capsule destroyed. She's trying to solve the poems and find out what we need to do about the box.'

'So it was her who led us to the first key?' asked Lisa.

'No,' corrected George. 'She told us where it was last. You led us to it, remember? With the crystal.'

'Does she know where the other two keys are?' asked Mark.

'She knows where one of them was hidden, and it's a place that I can't go to,' said George. 'It's the site of a famous battle in Roman times. Now it's the Fenn Street Children's Farm, especially for children. Old fogys like me are not allowed there.'

'That's alright, we'll go,' offered Mark.

'Not on your own,' said George. 'I'll ask Erica to take you.'

'Erica's not a child!' protested Mark.

'No, but she's young enough to get in,' said George. 'I'll tell her you're going to do some digging.'

'No, that's alright,' said Mark with a sigh of rueful resignation. 'We'll tell her.'

George took out a photograph of the missing key and handed it to Mark. He gave Lisa the crystal that she had used to find the first key at Kingston Market.

'Use this like before,' he said. 'It could save you a lot of digging. But be very careful; don't let anyone see you using it.'

Mark and Lisa promised to be careful and went outside.

'I'll go and find Erica,' offered Lisa.

'No,' said Mark, stopping her. 'I want to prove to Uncle George that we can do something properly without always having to be looked after like a couple of babies. He makes me feel like I can't do anything on my own. Also, when Erica sees what we're up to, she's bound to get suspicious. If we wanted to do some digging, we could do it here.'

'That's a point,' admitted Lisa.

'Come on,' he said. 'Let's find this Fenn Street place.'

As Mark and Lisa left the park, they didn't see the car parked opposite with the two Watchers inside it.

'There they are,' whispered the Watcher woman. 'All ready for us to grab!'

The woman Watcher was just about to drive the car towards Mark and Lisa, when the man stopped her.

'Wait! Why don't we see where they're going?'

'Perhaps they're going to look for the missing keys!' suggested the woman. 'If we get the children and the keys, it would make Sir Derek very pleased with us. Very pleased indeed.'

The man and woman watched as the two children carried on walking.

'I'll follow them and watch where they go,' said the man. 'You drive slowly and keep me in sight.'

Mark and Lisa walked on, unaware that they were being followed. The Fenn Street Children's Farm was only half-an-hour's walk away. When they got there, they found the warden. He pointed at an expanse of field near a fence.

'That area over there hasn't been dug up since Roman times,' he said. 'You can start there, if you like. But be careful: you might turn up something important.' And with that he left them to it.

Mark and Lisa walked over to the piece of ground. It was enormous.

'We'll never dig all this up!' scoffed Mark.

'We don't have to,' Lisa reminded him. 'We've got the power.'

'You don't really believe that, do you?' Mark said with disbelief.

'You saw what happened at the house. And how I found the first key using the crystal,' Lisa pointed out. 'And if we did have this power, it would save an awful lot of digging.'

Mark looked at the huge area of ground.

'I suppose it's worth a try,' he said reluctantly.

Lisa took the crystal in her hands and began to walk across the field, backwards and forwards.

The Watcher man and woman had parked outside the farm and were sitting inside the car waiting for the children.

'Why don't we go and get them?' said the man impatiently.

'Because it'll be easier to wait for them to come to us. They'll have to come out this way and they'll be nearer the car.'

Lisa was still walking to and fro across the field. Suddenly she stopped.

'I've got that feeling!' she said. 'It's here!'

'It's all rubbish,' grunted Mark.

'Take it!' ordered Lisa.

Reluctantly, Mark took the crystal.

'Well?' demanded Lisa.

'Maybe,' said Mark, and he started to dig.

After about ten minutes, they had a large hole, but no sign of the key.

'We'll be in Australia if we go down much more!' Mark complained. He carried on digging, but then stopped as he felt his spade hit something. He reached down into the hole and cleared the earth away from whatever it was. It was the key!

'Well?' demanded Lisa smugly. 'Do you still say it doesn't work?'

'That was amazing!' Mark admitted. 'It worked! It really worked!'

He put the key in his pocket and they headed back

towards the exit of the farm. That was when they saw the man and the woman, waiting for them by the exit.

The man got out of the car and forced a smile.

'Your Uncle George told us you'd be here,' he said. 'He sent us to pick you up and save you the walk home.'

Mark and Lisa didn't need to be reminded of what their mother had always told them about Don't Go With Strangers. There was definitely something nasty about these two. Mark and Lisa backed away, and then broke into a run.

'After them!' shouted the woman.

Mark and Lisa began to run faster. Behind them they could hear the heavy footsteps of the man closing in on them. Ahead of them was the fence. If they could only reach it . . .

At that moment, a man appeared in front of them. Mark and Lisa stopped and gasped in fear. Then their gasps changed to delight.

'Uncle George!' yelled Lisa.

'Get in the car,' barked George.

The Watcher man and woman stopped as they saw George. They turned and ran back to the exit and their waiting car.

The relieved Mark and Lisa looked at George.

'How did you know we were in danger, Uncle George?' asked Lisa.

'I didn't!' he replied in an angry tone. 'In your

stupidity at sneaking off like that, you forgot to cover yourselves. When I saw Erica still at work, I realised you two must have gone off on your own! It was stupid and dangerous! If I hadn't come along when I did, Heaven knows what would have happened to you.'

'We're sorry, Uncle George,' apologised Mark. 'We just wanted to do something on our own.' He grinned. 'Anyway, we did one thing right.' And he took the key from his pocket and held it up proudly.

They now had two of the keys. Where was the third? An hour later, after a visit to Anna and Ariana in the Crystal Capsule, George had the answer. The final key had been hidden by the original Guardian at the Roman baths in the town. He had made the key in the shape of a mosaic pattern and put it among the tiles that ran along the edge of the baths. To make it stand out in case it should ever be needed, he had marked the key tile with the letter G.

The old Roman baths had been turned into a museum long ago, and all the tiles and artefacts had been carefully stored away in glass display cases. That afternoon, George, Mark and Lisa took a trip there. They joined a guided tour and walked with the other visitors, listening as the guide talked about the history of the baths and how they were used in Roman times.

George, Mark and Lisa had memorised the pattern of

the missing key. It was here somewhere, George felt sure.

'There it is!' hissed Mark, and he hurried over to one of the glass display cases.

George and Lisa joined him at the case. Yes, there it was: a key, just like the other two, but with the same design as in the photograph! And in one corner, a letter G.

'But how do we get it?' asked Mark.

'Without causing a fuss!' said George, and he began taking photographs of the inside of the Roman baths.

Later, back at the house, George spread the photographs on the kitchen table. Mark and Lisa watched their Great Uncle, puzzled, as he began to examine them, muttering thoughtfully to himself.

'Laser beam connected to the burglar alarm . . . pressure pads on a separate system,' he murmured.

'Uncle George!' said Lisa, horrified as she realised what George was up to. 'You're thinking of stealing it!'

'I'm thinking of borrowing it,' George corrected her.

'It's still stealing!' insisted Lisa.

'No it isn't,' chimed in Mark. 'The box belongs to Uncle George: he's the Guardian. And this is the key to the box, so that also belongs to him. The fact that someone else found it and put it in a glass case doesn't alter the fact that it's still Uncle George's.'

'Have you thought of being a lawyer when you grow up, Mark?' smiled George, amused.

'Alright,' admitted Lisa. 'When you think of it like that, maybe it isn't stealing after all.'

'Possibly,' said George, 'but I still wouldn't like to try it as my defence if the police catch us.'

'So we are going to go in and get it?' asked Mark, very keen.

'We?' questioned George.

'Well, you did say you couldn't leave us on our own,' Mark pointed out.

'And we've got the powers you're going to need. You said so,' added Lisa.

George sighed. 'It looks like I'm up against tough opponents with you two. Okay, this is what we're going to do.' And he began to outline his plan, using the photographs.

That night, George, Mark and Lisa drove to the museum. Mark and Lisa watched in awe as George used his powers to short-circuit the wires of the burglar alarm system. He helped them through a window and into the museum.

Once inside, George put his finger to his lips to warn them to be quiet. He pointed at the security cameras, and, one by one, the red lights went off as George used his powers to shut them down.

'Right,' he whispered. 'Now to get the key.'

They crept alongside the glass cases until they came to the one that contained the final key. The key was on a stand right in the centre of the case.

'This is going to be difficult, very difficult,' said George. 'This case is wired up to pressure pads. Any sudden movement and all the alarms will go off.'

Mark and Lisa held their breath, not daring to move, as George carefully placed his fingers against the edge of the glass case and began to concentrate. There was a soft, low click. George opened his eyes and smiled. He had used his powers to unlock the display case! Very gently, he opened the glass lid, Mark picked up the key, and then, just as carefully, George closed the case shut.

'That was amazing!' said Mark, goggle-eyed.

'It certainly was!' said a voice behind them.

They turned, and came face to face with Dr Burns and three tough-looking men who had come out of the shadows.

THE CRYSTAL

CONNECTION

GEORGE, Mark and Lisa backed away from the three threatening figures.

'Hand it over,' said Burns, holding out her hand.

'Let's use our powers against them!' whispered Mark.

'No!' hissed George. 'We mustn't let the Watchers know that you two have powers.'

Burns and the three men came closer.

'Get the key off him,' Burns ordered two of the men.

The men rushed at George and grabbed him. As George struggled, his jacket fell open, and Burns gasped as she saw the other two keys hanging on the thong round his neck.

'We've got to do something!' cried Lisa.

Mark looked around frantically. Then he saw a nearby security alarm. He dashed over and hit it hard. Immediately the alarm went off.

The men stopped, shocked. This gave George the chance he needed to break free of their grip.

'Run!' he yelled.

George, Mark and Lisa made a run for the corridor,

which they knew would take them back to the window. Burns stood in their way, but George pushed her aside.

'After them!' yelled Burns.

'We've got to get out before the police come!' said one of the men. The burglar alarm carried on ringing.

'Alright, we'll get them later!' snarled Burns. 'Then I'll have my revenge on Mr George "Guardian" Gardner!'

On Heritron, the Supreme Taker was reviewing the situation with the Chief Catcher. Things were getting more desperate with each passing day, as machines shut down because of the lack of slaves to work them.

'The day after tomorrow the machines in the Western Province will be turned off every night,' said the Taker. 'In another week, they will be shut down completely.'

'And the other areas?' asked the Catcher.

'The month after, the Eastern Area, and then very quickly the other Provinces,' the Taker informed him gravely. 'We must have those slaves!'

'They will not be in time to save the Western Province,' pointed out the Catcher. 'Once we have more slaves, we will rebuild.'

The Catcher checked the charts on his wall. 'We have just six days left when the tunnel can be opened. We must get it opened – and now!'

At the Janus Foundation building, Sir Derek Janus was a very worried man. The Supreme Taker had just been in touch with him through the holographic communicator. Six days left, the Taker had said. The box must be opened now – or else! Janus shuddered. He knew exactly what that 'or else' meant: his life would be in torment. Still, Burns should be back any second with the keys.

The door of his office burst open and Dr Burns rushed in.

'At last!' said Janus, relieved. 'You have the keys?'

'No, sir,' gulped Burns. 'The boy raised the alarm.'

'What?' roared the angry Janus. 'I don't want excuses! I want the keys! Do you understand that? I must have those keys!'

'I nearly had them,' stammered Burns. 'All three of them.'

Janus stared at her, relief now on his face.

'You saw them?'

Burns nodded. 'Gardner has two of them round his neck, and the other he'd just taken from the Roman baths . . .'

'Excellent!' Janus shouted delightedly, interrupting her. 'All three keys!' His face took on a cunning expression. 'Now we'll get him, Burns! And with the keys! I have a plan!'

The next morning, Mark and Lisa were up bright and early to make breakfast. They could hear George busy at work in his study. It sounded like he was making something. Mark tapped at the study door and went in.

'Tea's made, Uncle George,' said Mark.

'Good,' said George. 'I'll have it in a minute when I've put the finishing touches to this.'

Lisa came in and joined Mark, and both of them went to see what George was doing. He had repaired the crystal mobile and was just hanging it up.

'There!' he said.

'What's that?' asked Lisa.

'It's a sophisticated communication system based on crystal technology,' said George.

He paused, and then carried on: 'You see, the last time I went to see Anna and Ariana, I was followed. I managed to give them the slip, but I can't take any more chances. With a bit of luck, I hope to use this to get in touch with the Crystal Capsule.'

'How does it work?' asked Lisa.

'The crystals will pick up my image in this room and send it to the Crystal Capsule, where Anna will pick it up in a similar device. But we know the Watchers have a device like this. The danger is they can use theirs to trace the signal and track down Anna and Ariana.'

'Like tracing a phone call?' asked Mark.

'Sort of. So all communication must be as brief as possible,' said George.

'Did I do much damage when I broke it?' asked Mark, guiltily.

'Some,' nodded George. 'I've done the best I can to mend it, but I'm afraid it'll only work intermittently. As I said, it's a very rare old piece, Mark. Irreplaceable. Spare parts don't just come off the shelf.'

Mark looked very upset.

'I'm so sorry, Uncle George,' he said miserably.

'Will it work for us too? Will we see them?' asked Lisa excitedly.

'As I said, if it works,' replied George.

'When are you going to try it?' Lisa continued, still feeling really excited.

'Well, I was going to do it now,' said George. He smiled playfully. 'But then Mark said something about breakfast being ready.'

The two children glared at him, outraged. He grinned.

'Okay. Let's try it,' he said.

George set the crystal mobile spinning. It began to spin faster and faster, and then, in the middle of the mobile, a moving picture began to form. It was a picture of Anna and Ariana. Mark and Lisa gasped in astonishment.

'Salutations, George,' said Anna. 'Ah, you must be Mark and Lisa. Salutations. So you are the Children

of Heritron. I do not envy you your task. The fate of your
world, and ours, is in your hands. I hope you are brave.'

'You're breaking up,' said Anna.

'Yes,' said George. 'The image is going. We must be
brief. The good news is that we've got all three keys.
Now we need to know what to do with them.'

'We will consult the poems,' said Anna.
'Communicate with us again shortly.'

Then the image faded.

Inside the Crystal Capsule, Anna sighed.

'Problems,' she muttered. She turned to Ariana. 'We'd better hurry and decipher this poem. We must be ready for George when he makes contact again.'

Ariana was already at work, scanning the poem, trying to solve its riddle. This one, though, seemed very clear and straightforward:

> *Take the keys, one two three*
> *And open the box, inside to see.*
> *Then shut the doors and lock them tight,*
> *Turn the keys with all your might.*

Half an hour later and Mark and Lisa were still gazing in awe at the mobile. The image of Anna and Ariana had faded, but they had still got the message. George thought over what Anna had told them.

'So now we know what I have to do. Open the box with the three keys and then re-lock it. And it will stay shut for ever.'

'It doesn't make sense,' grumbled Mark. 'It's already locked, so why have you got to open it again and then re-lock it? Why not just leave it shut?'

'I don't know either, Mark,' said George. 'Perhaps it's to do with re-sealing it. With a legend, nothing's simple. And remember, this is all part of an ancient legend, with everything foretold. If that's what the legend says, that's what we've got to do. Get to the box, open it, and then lock it for ever.'

'But Professor Waters has the box,' said Mark, 'and I can't see him letting us anywhere near it. Especially if he's one of these Watchers.'

'I'm not sure that he is,' said George thoughtfully. 'I just think he's got caught up in something that's out of his control.'

'How do we find out?' asked Mark.

'I think it's time we went to see the Professor and told him the whole story,' said George, putting on his coat.

'And at the same time, I think we should warn him about that assistant of his. That Dr Stephanie Burns,' Mark added.

George, Mark and Lisa drew up in George's car outside Waters' workshop just as the Professor was unlocking the doors to start work for the day.

'Professor Waters!' called George.

Waters glared at George and the two children as they got out of the car and came towards him.

'Well, Gardner?' snapped Waters. 'Say what you have to say, and then leave. I'm a very busy man.'

'Professor, I think it's time we sorted out our differences,' said George. 'I can open that box, but you need to know why it can't stay open.'

Waters gaped at him and then demanded: 'And why should I believe you?'

George took out the three keys and held them up.

'Because I have the keys.'

Waters didn't hesitate.

'Agreed!' he said. 'Let's get that box open!'

They all stepped inside his workshop, and Waters shut the door.

'Wait. Before we open it, I have to tell you what all this is about, and why I know so much about the box,' began George.

Waters looked at him suspiciously. 'Open the box first. There'll be plenty of time for explanations later.'

'It's important, Professor,' appealed Lisa.

'Very well,' said Waters. And he gestured for them to follow him into his office.

George hesitated, as if not knowing where to start, and then he began in a calm voice.

'That box,' he said, 'is more than it seems, Professor. It's a doorway to another world.'

'Oh really!' exclaimed the Professor in complete and utter disbelief.

George ignored the outburst and carried on, more insistently: 'It is a doorway to another world called Heritron . . .'

Professor Waters interrupted him angrily.

'Are you completely mad?' he spluttered.

George struggled to explain, but the Professor simply

refused to believe him. He waited until George had finished, and then he shook his head.

'I'm sorry, it's completely far-fetched,' said Waters at last. 'I don't believe a word of it.'

'But you must believe us. It really is the truth!' begged Lisa.

The Professor stood up and opened the door. 'I haven't the time to listen to this . . . this . . .'

Mark interrupted him quietly: 'We can prove it.'

They all turned to look at him.

'We can open the box,' he said, simply.

Waters nodded. 'Alright,' he said. 'Follow me.'

George, Mark and Lisa followed Waters out of his office. He led them along a corridor towards the room where the box was kept.

'It's in here,' said Waters, and he pushed open the door. Then Waters stopped, his face ashen. The room was empty. The box had gone!

Sir Derek Janus paced around his office. Where was Burns? Had she failed again? He daren't face the Supreme Taker until he had got hold of those keys.

There was a knock at his door.

'Come in!' he called.

It was Burns.

'The disposal team have the box,' she said. 'They should be here shortly.'

'Good,' said Janus. 'I have one other important job for you.'

Burns waited.

'The Supreme Taker believes that the rebel Anna is here in this world, in the Crystal Capsule,' said Janus. 'She will know the names of the two Children of Heritron mentioned in the legend, the ones who can seal Heritron's fate. These children must be found. The Taker has ordered me to find Anna and the Crystal Capsule, but we cannot! We've tried having the Guardian followed because we know he must be in contact with her, but the fools keep losing him!'

'What about the other one?' asked Burns. 'The Watcher you have placed close to the Guardian?'

'No luck there, yet, though she should succeed in time,' growled Janus. 'But we haven't got time! The Taker wants Anna found now! When we catch the Guardian, I am sure the Taker will force him to talk, but it all takes time that we have not got!'

Burns thought it over, and then she said: 'There is one way. Using holographic communicators leaves trace elements. Like a trail. If Anna is using a similar system as us to communicate with the Guardian . . .'

'. . . we can track her down!' realised Janus. 'That is excellent!'

'Providing the communicators are run for a certain length of time,' added Burns, cautiously.

'How long for?' asked Janus.

'Thirty seconds should give us the time to find out where the signal's coming from,' worked out Burns.

'Right! See to it!' Janus ordered. 'Set up a trace. With that, and our secret Watcher close to the Guardian, we should be able to track down the Crystal Capsule. And once we have the names of the two Children of Heritron, our enemies will be powerless to stop us!'

6 THE TRAP

GEORGE pushed past the stunned Professor Waters and hurried to the supports that had once held the box. Attached to them was a piece of paper.

'This is a repossession order for one box, the property of the Janus Foundation, of which they claim ownership by reason of funding granted to Professor Humphrey Waters,' he read.

'I'll sue them!' raged Waters. 'I'll fight them in court! I'll get that box back if it's the last thing I do! But I don't understand how they got in here.'

'Did anyone else have keys to this building?' asked George.

'Only my assistant, Dr Burns,' replied Waters.

George and the children exchanged rueful looks.

'Well, I think that answers that,' sighed Mark.

'What do you mean?' asked Waters.

They told him about Burns and her attack on them, and that she was working for Janus and the Watchers. Her working for Professor Waters had just been a cover to make sure the box was found and opened.

'Well,' shrugged George, 'now Janus has got the box, there's not much more we can do here.'

'There's plenty I can do!' stormed Waters.

They left the Professor shouting into the phone, demanding that the switchboard operator at the Janus Foundation put him through to Sir Derek Janus, but without success.

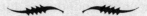

Back at the house, George told Mark and Lisa what he was planning to do.

'I'm going to get into the Janus Foundation building tonight.'

'And we're coming with you,' said Mark.

'Oh no you're not,' said George, firmly. 'You're staying here.'

'But we went with you to the Baths Museum!' pointed out Lisa.

'This is different,' said George. 'I'm going into the lion's den itself: the Janus Foundation. It's the Watcher's base. It's too risky. I daren't take you two in with me.'

'Well, we can't stay here on our own,' challenged Mark.

'You won't have to. I'll ask Erica if she'll do me a favour and stay here with you,' said George. 'I'll tell her I've got to go out somewhere overnight.'

Mark and Lisa looked crestfallen.

'Listen. You must understand. According to the

legend, you two children are vital. I must keep you safe,' said George.

'But what happens if you don't come back?' Lisa asked in a worried tone.

'I'll be back. And before midnight,' promised George.

That night at the Janus Foundation, Janus gave his orders to Burns and the other Watchers

'I want everyone to keep a watch out for Gardner. He is certain to come here tonight, bringing the keys with him. It is his destiny as the Guardian to try and save the Box of Destiny. Once he does, we shall catch him, and the keys will be ours.' He added a final warning: 'No one is to go near him until we are sure he is safely in. We don't want him getting away.'

With that, Janus and Burns returned to the office to keep a lookout for George on the security monitors.

Janus didn't know that George was already in the building and had used his powers to freeze the security system. He didn't know that the cameras would now only show images of empty corridors.

Unfortunately for George, he had nearly been caught by a security guard. He had heard someone approaching and had ducked into a room on the other side of the corridor. George had waited for the guard to go away, but instead he had gone into an office opposite and had begun to fill out forms!

George looked at his watch. It was nearly midnight. He had been stuck in this room for almost an hour. He knew that Lisa and Mark would be getting worried. If the guard didn't move soon, he would have to find some way to make him move!

Back at the house, Lisa looked at the clock beside her bed. Midnight, and George still hadn't returned. The sound of her door opening made her sit up, then she relaxed. It was Mark. He crept over to her bed so as not to wake Erica.

'It's gone midnight,' he whispered, worried. 'Uncle George said he'd be back by now.'

'I know,' replied Lisa. 'I've been wondering if there's something we could do.'

'What about if we tried Anna and Ariana in the Capsule, they might tell us what to do?' suggested Mark.

'How?' whispered Lisa. 'We don't know how that thing of Uncle George's works.'

'I think I do,' said Mark. 'I watched him set it going. I think I could get it to work. And it's better than just lying in this house doing nothing. I mean, terrible things could be happening to Uncle George. He might need our help, and we don't know!'

Lisa thought about it a bit more, then she nodded. Mark was right.

They crept downstairs and into George's study. Once inside, they shut the door, and then Mark got to work on the crystal mobile.

Inside the Crystal Capsule, Anna and Ariana were working out the latest poem, when the holographic communicator began to glow.

'It's George!' cried Ariana. 'He must have sealed the box! He's alright, after all!'

Then, instead of George, they saw the images of Mark and Lisa appear.

'Where's George?' asked Anna, worried. 'What's happened?'

'He's gone to this place called the Janus Foundation,' said Lisa. 'It's where the box has been moved to. He said it's where the Watchers' home is.'

Anna was shocked.

'The Janus Foundation? Oh no!' she cried. 'That's what this latest poem is about. It tells us that the Janus Foundation is a trap for George, and he's walking straight into it!'

As the image on the camera faded, Mark and Lisa looked at one another, horrified.

'I knew something was wrong!' cried Mark. 'We have to do something!'

'Let's wake up Erica,' suggested Lisa. 'We have to get someone to call the police and go to the Janus Foundation and save Uncle George, but no one will believe us because we're children. You know what adults are like.'

'Yes, including Erica,' Mark pointed out. 'She won't believe us either.'

'She might,' said Lisa.

'Might,' echoed Mark scornfully. 'You know what'll happen. Once we start telling her about the Takers and a doorway to another world, she'll just tell us it's our imaginations and not to be stupid. No, we're Uncle George's only hope.'

'What do you mean?' asked Lisa.

'Think about it,' said Mark. 'If we tell Erica and she doesn't believe us, then she won't let us do anything about it! No, we've got to go and find Uncle George ourselves and warn him that he's walking into a trap.'

At the Janus Foundation, the security guard was on the phone. George heaved a sigh of relief as he watched the guard put down the receiver and leave his office and continue on his rounds.

'Now to get to the box,' he murmured to himself.

In the office, Sir Derek Janus and Dr Burns were watching the security system, which still showed empty corridors.

'I don't understand it, sir,' said Burns, frowning. 'Surely we should see something. After all, our own people are searching the corridors for Gardner.'

The realisation of what was going on hit Janus.

'He's done something to the crystal circuit system!' he cried. 'He's frozen the images!'

'In that case, he must be here already!' said Burns.

'Go and check that the doorway is still safe!' Janus rasped. 'Then free the security devices!'

Outside the building, Mark and Lisa had arrived and

found the door that George had used to get into the building. He had left it slightly ajar ready for a quick exit. Mark and Lisa looked warily about them and then slipped silently into the building.

Inside Janus's office, Dr Burns returned.

'The doorway is still safe, Sir Derek,' she reported. 'And the security devices should be coming back on-line about now.'

As she spoke, they both looked at the security system, just in time to see Mark and Lisa creeping along a corridor.

Janus's face broke into a beam of delight.

'Well, well!' he crowed. 'This is even better! Get out there and get them!'

George guessed that the box would be in the most secure place, deep in the centre of the building. He crept silently along the empty corridors, keeping his eyes and ears open and checking every room in turn. Nothing.

He got to the last door and carefully opened it. The room was in darkness, but in the dim light he could see the box.

George moved swiftly into the room, taking the keys from round his neck as he did so.

At last! Three movements with the keys and the box would be sealed for ever! He was just about to put the first key in place, when the lights came on.

George whirled round. Standing there, smiling, were Sir Derek Janus and Dr Burns, and four others. And with them, held tightly, were Lisa and Mark.

'Welcome, Guardian!' grinned Janus. 'Now, hand over those keys!'

CHAPTER 7

THE BOX IS OPENED

'DON'T do it, Uncle George!' yelled Mark desperately.

'Do it, Guardian, or you know what will happen to them,' Janus said menacingly.

Reluctantly, George handed over the keys. Mark and Lisa looked aghast.

'You won't have them for long, Janus,' warned George. 'Your plan will fail.'

'Who's going to stop me?' sneered Janus. 'You with your powers?' He laughed, then turned to Dr Burns. 'Put the crystal amulet on him, Burns.'

Burns took a crystal bracelet from her pocket and held it in a gloved hand. As she came near George, it glowed.

'It's a restraining crystal,' explained Janus. 'It will neutralise your powers.'

George began to back away. Suddenly, the room began to vibrate.

'He's using his powers! Stop him!' shouted Janus.

George shot a look at Mark and Lisa. He had realised

what was happening: the twins were starting to use their powers.

'No!' shouted George at them.

Luckily, Janus thought George was shouting at Burns. Burns pounced and placed the glowing crystal amulet on George's wrist. George winced, as though he had been burned.

'There!' said Janus, satisfied. 'Now take them away and lock them up. We'll deal with them later!'

As soon as the three had been locked in a room in the basement, George turned on Mark and Lisa.

'You pair of idiots!' he stormed. 'Why on earth did you come here?'

'Because we found out it was a trap,' explained Lisa.

'Of course it was a trap!' snapped George. 'I knew that and I'd planned for it, but I'd still have been able to re-lock the box whatever happened!' He groaned. 'You idiots! Now the box will be opened!'

'Because you gave him the keys,' replied Mark angrily. 'You shouldn't have! We could have done something. Fought back.'

'Like you started to, and what would have happened then?' demanded George. 'He would have realised that you're not just ordinary children and that you have the power; that you two are the Children of Heritron named in the legend. And that would have been the end of you.'

'What's the use of having this power if we're not allowed to do anything with it?' Mark groaned.

'You'll use it when the time is right,' said George.

'When will that be?'

'I don't know,' George admitted.

'We're sorry, Uncle George,' said Lisa apologetically. 'We only came here to save you.'

'I know,' sighed George. 'I'm sorry I got angry. You did it with a good heart.'

'Can't we get out of here and shut the box again?' asked Mark.

'Not with this thing on me,' said George ruefully. 'This crystal strips me of my powers.'

'Can we get it off?' asked Lisa, reaching towards it.

George shook his head. 'No! Don't touch it.'

Lisa backed away.

'I'm afraid not,' said George. 'It needs someone else with stronger powers. Someone who can control them. And the only one who can do it is Anna.'

'So we've got to get you to the Crystal Capsule!' said Lisa. 'Uncle George, we do have the power! I'm sure we can use it to get us out of here!'

'And they won't think it's us. They'll think you did it in some way,' added Mark.

'Well, we've got nothing to lose,' said George. 'You may as well try.'

In his office, Janus was talking to the Supreme Taker on the holograph.

'The box is open, Your Excellency. The Catchers can come through. You can take the slaves from this world at will.'

'Well done, Janus. You will be well rewarded,' said the Taker approvingly. 'And what of the Guardian?'

'We have him. And he has been neutralised so he cannot use his powers.'

'Excellent!' said the Taker triumphantly. 'Bring him to me! I shall interrogate him and find out where this Crystal Capsule is. Then we shall have everything. The names of the two children, and the destruction of the rebels Anna and Ariana!'

Inside the basement room, Mark and Lisa concentrated on trying to open the locked door.

'I can feel it . . . something . . . moving,' murmured Lisa.

'Relax. Don't force it . . . just let it happen,' advised George.

Mark scowled.

'It's no good! It doesn't work when we try and make it work, only when we don't!'

'The trick is to make it work when you want to, not just haphazardly,' George gently remarked. 'Calm down. Try it again.'

The children placed their hands against the door and tried again.

'Just concentrate on the lock,' said George quietly. 'Think of it . . . picture it . . . the different parts . . . the mechanism . . . think of it moving . . . slowly . . . gently . . . no force, no pressure . . . think . . . the metal parts just slide open easily . . . easily . . . the bolt slides up . . . and . . .'

There was a click from the lock. Mark and Lisa looked at each other in surprise. Then Lisa turned the handle, and the door opened!

'Right,' said George. 'Now to get out of here and get this thing off me.'

Sir Derek Janus hurried back to the room that held the box.

'I am about to open the Box of Destiny,' he announced to the waiting Watchers, 'and then I am going through the doorway.'

'You?' gaped Burns.

'I have been summoned,' Janus told them proudly. 'Fetch the Guardian and bring him through after me. The Takers wish to question him.'

Burns hesitated.

'Wouldn't it be better to wait and go through with the Guardian?' she asked warily.

'No!' said Janus firmly. 'No one has set foot through

that box for nearly two thousand years! I will be the first! This is my moment of triumph! I will not share it. The Guardian can be brought through after me, like the slave he soon will be!'

He stepped over to the box and began to place the three keys in the lid. That done, he turned the handle, and the box opened, revealing a bright glow inside. Smoke began to curl out from inside the box and a vast doorway appeared in the room. The tunnel was formed.

'At last!' Janus said. 'My moment of triumph!'

He opened the giant doorway and stepped inside the tunnel.

Mark and Lisa followed George down the alley, past the decaying buildings. Getting out of the Janus Foundation had been easier than expected. Everyone had been watching the box, and no one had expected them to be able to get out of the locked room.

George stopped at the shop that housed the Crystal Capsule. He pushed open the wooden door and ushered in Mark and Lisa. They followed him to the back of the old shop and through the misty haze behind the door.

When Anna saw that Mark and Lisa were with George, she shook her head, concerned.

'George, is it wise to bring them here?' she asked.

'Possibly not, but we're being left with fewer and fewer alternatives,' admitted George. 'If anything happens to me, Mark and Lisa have to know how to find you.'

'Why, what's happened?' asked Anna.

There was an awkward pause, then George told Anna and Ariana what had happened: the Watchers opening the box and his powers being neutralised. Shamefacedly, he revealed the crystal on his wrist.

Anna put on a glove to protect herself from the effect of the crystal, then removed the crystal from George's skin and put it safely away in a drawer.

'What can we do now that the Watchers have opened the box?' asked Mark.

'According to the next poem, we think Professor Waters is the answer,' said Ariana.

She showed them the poem:

> *When the precious falls*
> *into wrong hands wrench it*
> *back with force, aqua!*

'Aqua was the Roman word for water,' she explained. 'We think it means that somehow he has the ability to get the box back.'

'Right,' said George, grimly. 'First thing tomorrow morning we'll call on Professor Waters and see what he can do.'

80

Janus stepped out the end of the tunnel. Heritron! At last, after nearly two thousand years, a Watcher had returned to Heritron!

The Chief Catcher was waiting for him in the room that housed the end of the tunnel.

'Salutations and welcome,' said the Catcher. 'Her Excellency the Supreme Taker is waiting for you in the Control Room.'

'Wait!' pleaded Janus. 'This is my first sight of my Home World. Please, just let me take it in for a moment.'

The Catcher hesitated. He didn't want to risk upsetting the Taker. But then he nodded.

Janus went to the window and looked out. Heritron! Before him was a weird and wonderful world. Huge castle towers soared from a dense, dark jungle that shimmered in a strange light. The sky was an unusual colour too, as if it were never quite day here yet never quite night. Janus noticed a dreadful sense of decay. Buildings looked as if they might soon fall down, and everywhere the jungle seemed to be taking over again. Vines and creepers clambered up the walls of the towers and clung to the ramparts. What few lights there were, glowed dimly.

The Catcher saw the look of dismay on Derek Janus's face.

'Repairs are needed everywhere,' he said. 'Now you see why we need the slaves so urgently.'

'What happened to all the slaves before?' asked Janus. 'Surely they should have bred and produced more?'

'They did, but as time went on there were no more new slaves. Now our slaves are weak, too weak to do the work we need, and they are beginning to die out.' The Catcher tapped Janus on the shoulder. 'Come, it does not do to keep Her Excellency waiting.'

Janus turned and followed the Catcher.

The Supreme Taker was standing surveying the schedules of Slave Labour as the Catcher and Janus came into the Control Room. She began to smile in welcome, then the smile disappeared as she noticed that Janus didn't have George with him.

'Where is the Guardian?' she demanded.

'He will be following, Your Excellency. Under guard. I could not wait to be in your presence. And I wanted a Watcher to be the first through the doorway, after all this time.'

The Taker nodded.

'I understand,' she said. 'You have done well, Janus.'

She was interrupted by a beeping and a flashing light from the holographic communicator.

'Incoming message, Your Excellency,' announced the Catcher.

Janus bowed. 'I will leave you, and return when you are free.'

'No need, Janus,' replied the Taker. 'The message is from your own building.'

Janus frowned, puzzled. Then the image of Burns appeared on the machine. She looked distressed.

'Speak,' commanded the Taker.

'Your Excellency . . . the Guardian . . .' stammered Burns.

'Yes. We await him,' said the Taker.

Burns hesitated, then she blurted out: 'I regret to report that he has escaped.'

The Supreme Taker whirled on Janus, fury in her eyes.

'Escaped?' she roared.

Janus shrank back in fear.

'I used the disarming amulet!' he protested. 'The Guardian had no powers!'

'Then how did he get away?' the Taker said in a hoarse growl.

'We are searching the building,' gulped Burns. 'He cannot have got out.'

'Unless he had help,' accused the Taker.

'A traitor, amongst the Watchers? Impossible,' stammered Janus.

'What about the two children? His niece and nephew?' suggested Burns. 'Perhaps they have the power. Could they be the two referred to in the legend who can "seal the fate of Heritron for ever"?'

The Supreme Taker shook her head. 'No, the legend refers to the two who can do that as the "Children of Heritron". These two are Earthling children. No, in some way the Guardian received help from the rebels Anna and Ariana.'

'But we saw no sign of them!' protested Janus.

'That means nothing!' snarled the Taker. 'No, I sense rebel hands in this. Anna must be found! Return to Earth at once. It is now even more imperative that you find the Crystal Capsule and get me the names of those children so that we may capture them. And then destroy Anna and the Crystal Capsule!'

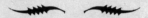

George, Mark and Lisa were almost at George's house, when they stopped. There was a light on in the kitchen.

'They'll know by now we've got away,' whispered Mark. 'Perhaps they're in there waiting for us.'

'That's what I'm thinking!' said George grimly. 'You two stay behind me.'

George crept towards the back door of the house. He opened it and then crept towards the kitchen without a sound. Yes, there was definitely someone moving about in there!

George flung the door open – and saw Erica in her dressing gown.

'George!' she yelped. 'Thank heavens you're back! Mark and Lisa are missing! I heard noises and I went to check on them, and they were gone! I was going to give it another five minutes and then phone the police, but I thought I'd wait and see if you came back first.'

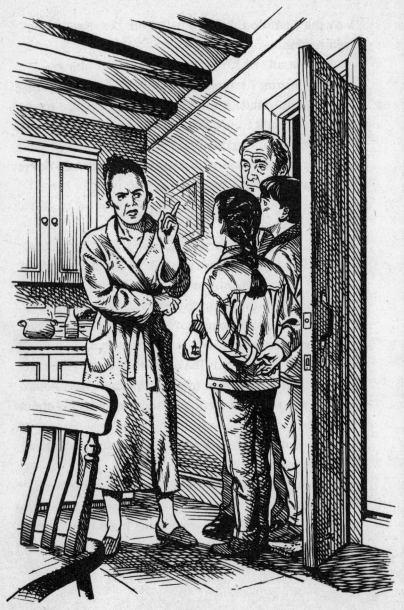

Mark and Lisa appeared in the kitchen doorway behind George.

'It's alright, Erica. We're here!' they said.

Erica glared at them.

'Where have you been?' she demanded. 'I've been worried out of my mind!'

'It's my fault, I'm afraid, Erica,' said George thinking quickly. 'I'd been badger-watching and I actually found some badgers. I was so excited I came back for the children to show them, but I didn't want to wake you.'

Erica stared at him.

'But . . .' she began.

'I'm sorry, I didn't mean to worry you,' apologised George. 'I thought you'd be asleep.'

Erica glared at him, and at Mark and Lisa.

'You should have left a note or something,' she said, still sounding angry. 'Like I said, I've been dreadfully worried!'

'I know. I'm sorry,' George said again. 'I was totally in the wrong. I just didn't expect you to be up at this hour. Forgive me?'

Erica scowled for about two seconds more, and then she smiled.

'Alright,' she said. 'So long as next time you go out badger-watching, you take me with you.'

'Deal,' grinned George. He turned to Mark and Lisa and said cheerfully: 'Right, kids. Bed. I think we could all do with some sleep.'

'I'll just clear up here before I go up,' said Erica. 'I'd just made myself a cup of tea to calm my nerves.'

Erica watched them go up the stairs. Then she turned and hurried to the phone. With one ear listening in case George or the children came back, she telephoned Sir Derek Janus's private number.

Dr Burns answered it.

'Hello?' said Burns.

'Tell Sir Derek the Guardian and the children have returned here. I shall make sure I get the information he needs.'

Erica was a Watcher!

CHAPTER 8

INTO THE BOX

FIRST thing the next morning, George, Mark and Lisa drove to the workshop to see Professor Waters. Without telling him that their information came from the Crystal Capsule, George urged the Professor to join forces and work with them.

'It's the only way we're going to get that box back!' he said.

'Well, that's where you're wrong!' retorted Waters. 'In fact, I expect to have it back here very shortly. At this very moment, my solicitors are getting a court order for the return of that box. And frankly, I can do without you and your bizarre theories of what's in it.'

George was relieved when he heard about the court action. Perhaps this was what Anna had meant when she said Waters was the one who could get the box back.

'You may get the box back, Professor,' he said, 'but you'll still need me to open it.'

Just then the phone rang. Waters was quick to pick

up the receiver. He listened briefly, and then he smiled and hung up.

'That was my solicitors,' he announced. 'They've got the court order to get the box back. I'm going to meet them at the Janus Foundation now. That box will be back here within the hour.'

'Still locked shut,' George pointed out.

Waters thought this over, then he nodded.

'Very well,' he agreed. 'I'll telephone you when the box is back here. But if you're wasting my time and you can't open it, I warn you, I'll have you thrown out of here quicker than you can say abracadabra.'

As George and the children left Waters' workshop, Mark scowled: 'Huh! I can't see the Watchers just letting the police go in and take the box back, just like that!'

'It might just work,' mused George. 'I don't think the Watchers will risk using their telekinetic powers against the police. They won't want to show their hand and do anything that might suggest that something out of the ordinary is going to happen.'

'But say Professor Waters does get the box back. How are you going to open it and then re-lock it? You haven't got the keys any more,' Lisa pointed out.

George shrugged.

'I'm keeping my fingers crossed the keys will still be with the box,' he said.

At the Janus Foundation, Sir Derek Janus was standing next to the box and instructing the Watchers on their next move.

'Although we still have to find the Crystal Capsule and the rebel Anna, the fact that the doorway is now open means that the Catchers can come through and begin to take children back to Heritron,' he told them. 'Even as I speak, the Catchers are preparing. We have to make sure that when they bring the children they catch back here . . .'

The ringing of the phone interrupted him. Annoyed, Janus snatched up the receiver and barked into it: 'I said I wasn't to be disturbed!'

'I'm sorry, Sir Derek, but the police are here,' said the security guard on duty at the reception desk.

Janus gaped, incredulous. The police!

'They're with a Professor Waters,' continued the security guard. 'They've got a court order to take possession of a box. They say it's stolen property.'

Burns had overheard this and she shook her head in horror. 'We can't let them up here, Sir Derek! We must resist them! Fight!'

'And arouse their suspicions about what's really going on?' said Janus. 'Don't be a fool, Burns! I'll see if I can talk them out of it. If not, we'll just have to let them take the doorway. But don't worry, we'll get it back very soon.' To the security guard he said: 'Send them up.'

'They're already on their way, sir,' said the guard.

'Quickly, close the box,' ordered Janus.

The next minute, the door opened and Waters rushed in, closely followed by a force of policemen. Burns rushed to the box and took the keys out, determined to hide them, but she was spotted by Waters.

'Stop that woman!' he shouted. 'Those items are part of the box!'

The sergeant who was leading the policemen stepped in front of Burns and held out his hand.

'I'll have to take those as well, I'm afraid,' he said.

'Look, Sergeant,' smiled Janus, 'a mistake has been made. That box belongs to the Janus Foundation, of which I am the chairman. We have proved that the funding to retrieve it came from us, so . . .'

'I'm sorry, sir. I'm just carrying out my instructions,' said the sergeant.

He gestured to the other policemen, who picked up the box.

'Look, if you just wait one moment while I phone my solicitors,' continued Janus, desperately.

'I'm sorry, sir, I can't go against the order of the court,' said the sergeant. 'Take it out, men!'

As the box was lifted and carried out, Janus and Burns glared at the smiling Waters.

'You won't have it for long!' snarled Janus, menacingly.

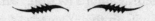

George put down the phone and turned to Mark and Lisa with a triumphant smile.

'That was Professor Waters. He's got the box! Let's go!'

Waters was standing by the box when they arrived at the workshop. He was holding the three keys and looking very frustrated.

'Impressive security,' George complimented Waters. The three of them had noticed the security cameras and the guard on duty as they entered the building.

'No one's going to take this away from me now, I can assure you!' said Waters. He looked at the three keys and scowled. 'These keys don't work!'

'Allow me,' said George.

He took the keys from Waters and inserted each one in its place, one after the other.

'They have to go in the right order, like a combination lock,' he explained.

As George put the last key in place, Waters impatiently tugged at the lid of the box. The lid remained firmly shut.

'They still don't work!' wailed Waters.

George smiled, amused at Waters' anguish.

'Like any door, Professor, there's also a door handle,' he said.

George turned one of the other designs on the lid, and the box opened, revealing the entrance to the tunnel.

Waters' expression changed from eager anticipation to one of sheer astonishment as he saw the vast doorway to Heritron appear. Mark and Lisa also looked stunned.

'What on earth!' gaped Waters.

'Now do you believe me?' said George, softly.

He began to shut the lid again, but the angry Waters stopped him.

'It's a trick of some sort!' he shouted. 'And now it's opened, I'm not having it shut again!'

'It's a doorway that simply has to be kept shut!' George insisted.

'It's my box and as far as I'm concerned you've played your part,' said Waters defiantly. 'This is just some sort of optical illusion. Now you've opened it, you can go!'

Mark and Lisa looked at their Great Uncle, wondering what he was going to do.

'Out! Before I call my security people and have them throw you out!' shouted Waters.

'I can't let you do that, I'm afraid, Professor,' sighed George.

'Oh can't you! Well, let me see you try!' snapped Waters, and he reached for the phone to call his security guard.

George headed towards a button marked 'Alarm'. He was just about to press it, when George used his telekinetic powers. Waters found himself being hurled by an invisible force into an observation booth. The door of the booth slammed shut, and locked itself.

'I hate to do this, Professor Waters, but you leave me no choice,' George said apologetically.

While Waters banged helplessly on the window of his office, George went to the box, shut the lid and re-locked it with the three keys.

'There! Locked again!'

He took out the three keys and looked at them determinedly.

'Now to destroy these so it can never be opened again,' he announced.

Just before they went, he pulled at the door handle to make sure the door was firmly locked – and it opened!

George, Mark and Lisa gazed at the open box in dismay.

'Maybe it needs a different combination to close it?' asked Lisa.

'Maybe,' said George. He looked rather worried. 'Or maybe there's something we don't know about it. I think we have to get in touch with Anna and Ariana. If anyone knows how to lock that box again, they will. Come on.'

'But what about the Professor?' asked Lisa.

George looked at the Professor, still banging helplessly on the soundproof glass.

'For the moment, he's safer there than with the box,' he commented.

Back at the house, George set the holographic communicator working. Immediately, it triggered a signal in the Communications Room at the Janus Foundation building.

'Anna and the Guardian are communicating!' cried Burns, who had been monitoring the signal.

'Excellent!' said Janus. 'We need a fix to find the position of the Crystal Capsule!'

Burns watched as the signal pointers criss-crossed on the screen in front of her, narrowing the position down.

'Well?' snapped Janus impatiently.

'I'm trying, sir, but they keep breaking off communication,' said Burns.

The screen went dead.

'Lost them!' groaned Burns. 'I'm sorry, sir.'

Janus was absolutely furious. 'Get someone to monitor that signal all day and all night if necessary,' he barked.

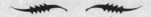

At the workshop, Waters had eventually been released from the observation booth by the security guard, who had come in on his routine check.

'Why didn't you come here before?' demanded Waters.

'That man said you weren't to be disturbed,' explained the guard.

'I bet he did!' stormed Waters. 'Well, if he comes back, don't let him in. Under any circumstances!'

With that, Waters sent the guard back to his desk in the reception area. Then he approached the box. He opened it and the doorway to Heritron appeared. He approached the vast doors with caution and pulled them open.

Intrigued, Waters stepped in and began to walk along the tunnel.

At George's house, George and the two children reflected on the latest news from Anna and Ariana in the Crystal Capsule. According to their solving of the latest poem, someone had to go through the door into the box, and then lock the other door at the end of the tunnel, the one at the Heritron end. And those 'someones' were Mark and Lisa!

'Anna must have got this one wrong,' said George.

'No, she hasn't,' said Lisa. 'I clearly remember what she said:

> *'This will be the time*
> *For the Children of Heritron.*
> *Go through the first door.*
> *To the second door.*
> *Turn the keys.'*

Lisa looked at George. 'That means us. You said yourself, Mark and I are the Children of Heritron.'

'I don't care what the poem says,' said George rather flatly. 'It's too dangerous. I can't put you at risk like that. I don't believe it makes any difference who closes the door, so long as it's closed. I'm going to do it.'

'But the poem said . . .' began Mark in protest.

'I know what it said, and I know what I'm saying,' insisted George. 'You are not going through into that tunnel. I am.'

'What tunnel?' queried Erica, intrigued.

They turned and saw that Erica had appeared at the doorway of the study.

'Er, badger tunnels,' lied George, thinking quickly.

'You're not taking them badger-watching again?' asked Erica.

'Er, no, not this time. Just me,' smiled George. 'Actually, would you mind staying overnight again, Erica, to look after the children, just in case I get held up? Badger-watching can take hours. You never know when they're going to turn up! Unpredictable little creatures.'

'Alright,' agreed Erica. 'But I've got to make a phone call first. I was supposed to be seeing my sister tonight. Is it alright if I use your phone?'

'Of course,' nodded George.

Erica headed for the kitchen and the phone. George winked at Mark and Lisa. They didn't wink back. They were the ones who were supposed to go through the tunnel, not Uncle George! They knew he was wrong.

The frantic ringing of the doorbell made them all hurry to the front door. It was Professor Waters and he was out of breath and shocked.

'I went into the tunnel!' he blurted out. 'It was like you said. Another world. It was terrifying!'

George, worried that Erica would hear, carefully steered Waters into the study.

Once there, Waters told them about going into the

tunnel, and peering through the partly opened door at the other end, and seeing the Catchers already waiting to come through, and talking about getting as many slaves as possible.

'Now you see why I have to go through and shut it off completely,' George told him when he had finished.

'Yes, I see that now,' agreed Waters. 'But can you do it?'

'I can and I will,' said George. 'You stay here and recover while I go to your workshop, Professor.'

'I can't!' said Waters urgently. 'I'll have to come with you. I gave my security people instructions not to let you in.'

George and Waters headed for the door.

Lisa and Mark looked worried.

'Are you sure you're going to be alright, Uncle George?' asked Lisa.

'Don't worry,' George reassured them. 'I'm not going into the other world. I'm just going as far as the end of the tunnel to lock the door. I should be quite safe. After all, they won't be expecting me.'

In the kitchen, Erica was finishing a whispered phone call to Sir Derek Janus.

'That's right, I overheard them. The Guardian's going into the tunnel, right to the far end. Now is the Takers' chance to catch him once and for all!'

Waters and George headed back to the workshop. Once there, they looked at the open box, and at the tunnel, glowing mysteriously.

George turned to Professor Waters and asked him to make a solemn promise.

'If anything goes wrong, I want you to make me a promise. I want you to stay here until I get back. And, if I'm not back by the morning, then I want you to go to the children. They'll know what to do.'

'I promise,' agreed Waters.

'And if that happens, I want you to take care of them until their mother returns,' added George.

Waters nodded.

'I will,' he said. He shook George's hand firmly. 'I was a fool to not believe you before. A lot of precious time has been wasted.'

'Let's hope I can recover it,' said George. He took the three keys in his hand, all ready. 'Remember, look after the children.'

And with that he stepped into the tunnel.

The tunnel twisted and turned, bending this way and that, the light at the far end getting brighter all the time. Finally, George made it. The door at the other end was partly open, light filtering through.

George reached the door and silently pulled it shut. He nervously began to fit the three keys into their positions: the first key, the second key . . .

At that moment, the door was wrenched open and

George found himself grabbed by the arms and hauled into the strange world of Heritron. Two men held him; they looked like soldiers by their dress. The Catcher smiled grimly.

'Welcome, Guardian,' he said. 'We've been expecting you. The Supreme Taker has wanted to meet you for a long, long time.'

NEITHER Lisa nor Mark slept much that night: they were both worried about George. As dawn broke, he still hadn't returned.

'What do we do?' asked Lisa.

'I think we ought to get in touch with the Crystal Capsule,' suggested Mark. 'Let Anna and Ariana know what's happened. Anna will know what to do.'

'What about Erica? Do you think we ought to tell her?' asked Lisa.

'Let's talk to Anna first,' said Mark.

They walked across the hallway to George's study, opened the door, and then stopped, shocked. The crystal mobile was lying on the floor, smashed.

'Oh no!' cried Mark. 'What are we going to do now?'

Just then Erica appeared.

'You two are up early,' she yawned.

Then she saw the smashed crystal mobile and let out a gasp of horror.

'What have you two done?' she cried. 'You know you shouldn't have touched that!'

'It wasn't us!' protested Mark.

'Well who else was it?' asked Erica. She let out a groan. 'I'm going to get the blame for this. I was left in charge!'

Just then the doorbell rang. Erica got up to answer it.

'Maybe it's Uncle George?' said Lisa hopefully.

It wasn't. It was Professor Waters.

As Waters stepped in, the phone rang. Erica rushed to answer it.

Mark and Lisa hurried to ask Waters if there was any news about George.

'He hasn't come back, I'm afraid,' said Waters sadly. 'His last words were that if he didn't come back, I was to come and tell you two. He said you would know what to do.'

Mark and Lisa looked as if they were about to cry. Just then Erica called.

'Your mother's on the phone.'

Mark and Lisa looked at each other. They had to pull themselves together, pretend everything was normal. They dare not worry their mother. They had to find a way to find out what had happened to George.

As Mark and Lisa went to the phone, Erica found Professor Waters examining the broken crystal mobile.

'Leave that alone!' she snapped.

'But I'm sure I've seen something similar. It's Roman. I'm certain of it. Priceless,' said Waters. 'I may be able to fix it.'

'I said leave it alone! George left me in charge here and I'm in enough trouble that it's been broken like that. I don't want you interfering and making it worse.'

On the phone, Mark was trying to pretend that everything was alright.

'No, we're fine here, Mum . . . Everything's fine . . . No, Uncle George isn't here at the moment . . . No, he's not far away, he's only popped out for a second . . . We're not on our own . . . Erica's here . . . and Professor

Waters . . . The house is full of adults . . . You'll be here this evening. Right. We'll see you then. Bye.'

He hung up and turned to Lisa.

'She's on her way back. She'll be here this evening,' he told her. And then he groaned: 'What do we do now?'

'George told the Professor we'd know what to do,' said Lisa. 'He said we were to tell Anna if he didn't come back.'

'Right,' nodded Mark. 'Then let's go and see her.'

Mark and Lisa returned to the study, where they found Erica and Waters still arguing over the broken crystal. Waters was insisting that he might be able to mend it, and Erica was insisting that he left it where it was.

'We've . . . er . . . we've got to go out. We won't be long,' said Mark.

'Out? Where?' demanded Erica.

'Just on an errand,' said Lisa. 'It's something Uncle George wanted us to do.'

'Okay. I'll come with you,' said Erica.

'There's no need for you to come, Erica,' smiled Mark, trying to put her off.

'Oh yes there is,' insisted Erica. 'Your Uncle George left me in charge. That means I'm responsible for your safety. You're certainly not going wandering around the streets on your own.'

Mark and Lisa looked at Waters, silently appealing

for his help. Waters realised at once that where they were going had something to do with George.

'I'll go with them, wherever it is!' he offered.

Mark and Lisa's relief was short-lived.

'Certainly not!' said Erica indignantly. 'George left you both in my care. If you won't accept what I say about this matter, then I'll have to phone your mother and tell her that something is going on here and let her decide who you two can go off with. Because something is going on, and you can't tell me differently. Well?'

Mark and Lisa sagged, defeated. They looked at each other, and then nodded in agreement. They'd have to trust Erica.

'Okay,' said Mark. 'But we haven't got a lot of time. We'll tell you everything on the way.'

At his office, Sir Derek Janus was listening to the Supreme Taker via the holographic communicator.

'The Guardian is stubborn,' said the Taker. 'I have questioned him but he refuses to tell us where the Crystal Capasule is. The Catchers are ready to come through. We need to know that the Crystal Capsule has been found. We can take no chances that the rebels will interfere with our plan. Now we have the Guardian, only Anna and the Children of Heritron can defeat us. You must find the Crystal Capsule.'

'It is already being done, Your Excellency,' Janus

answered, calmly. 'As we speak, our plan to locate the Crystal Capsule is already in operation.'

As Erica drove, Mark and Lisa told her the whole story.

'So, if we can't shut the doorway, then the Catchers will come through,' said Mark. 'And that's where we're going now. To find out how to shut it.'

'And save Uncle George,' added Lisa.

Erica pretended to look bewildered by all this.

'But this is all . . . all . . . weird!' she said.

'That's how we felt when Uncle George told us,' admitted Mark. 'But you'll believe it when you've met the others.'

'Others?'

'Pull up at this corner,' said Lisa. 'We walk from here.'

Erica parked the car, then Mark and Lisa led her down the alleyway, past the derelict buildings, until they came to the old ruined shop.

'In here,' said Lisa.

They went in, through to the back of the dusty shop, and then through the wall of shimmering haze behind the door.

Anna and Ariana were just checking the ninth poem as Mark, Lisa and Erica walked into the Crystal Capsule. Anna's smile of welcome vanished as she saw Erica.

'Who's this?' she demanded, worried.

'This is Erica,' explained Lisa. 'She can be trusted.'

As Erica wandered around the shelves of books, Anna took Mark and Lisa aside and whispered urgently to them: 'I do not like this. Bringing a stranger in like this. She could be anyone. It was not wise.'

'We didn't have a choice,' muttered Mark apologetically. 'George left us in her care, and he hasn't come back from the tunnel.'

'What? But it was supposed to be you two who went!' exclaimed Anna.

'That's what we told him, but he wouldn't let us go,' Lisa told her.

'But why didn't you use the communication device to get in touch?' asked Anna.

'It's broken,' replied Mark gloomily. 'Do you think the Takers have got George?'

'I am very much afraid so,' said Anna sadly.

'So that's what this poem has been about,' exclaimed Ariana. Erica rejoined them as Ariana showed Mark and Lisa the poem:

> *The twins of Heritron*
> *Will be the Guardian's friend.*
>
> *A friend will do*
> *What others won't,*
> *A friend will come and find you.*

'What a strange poem,' remarked Erica. 'Who are the twins of Heritron?' she asked, pretending to be innocent.

'We are,' replied Lisa.

Anna was alarmed by Erica's interest. 'It's just a pet name,' she said hurriedly. 'It means nothing.'

But Erica understood only too well what it meant. Mark and Lisa were the Children of Heritron who they so deparately needed to find.

Ariana was still explaining the poem to Mark and Lisa.

'It means you have to go through to Heritron and rescue George,' she said.

'But how will we find him when we get to Heritron?' asked Mark. 'He could be anywhere? We don't even know if he's still alive!'

'Yes, he is,' said Anna.

She produced a piece of crystal and handed it to Mark. It glowed faintly in his hand.

'This crystal will help you,' she told them. 'While it glows, it shows he's still alive. The nearer you get to him, the brighter the glow. Follow it. Use it to find George.'

'Come on, let's go,' said Mark, slipping the crystal into his pocket.

'Where to?' asked Erica.

'We have to go into the tunnel.'

'I'll come with you,' said Erica.

Lisa and Mark shook their heads.

'No,' said Lisa. 'It's something we have to do on our own.'

Erica nodded. 'Anyway, at least I can drive you there. Come on.'

Anna and Ariana watched them leave. Both of them had worried expressions on their faces. They were worried for George, and they were worried for Mark and Lisa. And now Anna was worried about Erica. There was something not quite right about her. She didn't trust her.

Back in Erica's car, Mark and Lisa were driving along when they noticed that Erica seemed to be going the wrong way.

'You've missed the turning, Erica,' said Lisa. 'To get to the Professor's workshop you should have taken that turning back there.'

Erica laughed, and it was a menacing sort of laugh that sent chills down their backs.

'But we're not going to the Professor's workshop,' she said. 'You're coming to meet some friends of mine. They've been dying to meet the Children of Heritron!' Then she laughed again. 'Sir Derek and the others thought the legend meant two children actually on Heritron, but it meant you two! All this time, and you were right under our noses!'

Mark and Lisa started tugging at the door handles, but they didn't move.

'Child locks,' Erica smirked. 'Very useful.'

And she started to laugh again.

Mark and Lisa began to bang on the car windows
and shout, but it was no use: no one could hear them.
And, at the speed they were travelling, there was
nothing they could really do. They were trapped!

'Let us out! Stop the car!' shouted Mark. 'If you don't
stop, we'll make you stop,' warned Mark coldly.

Mark closed his eyes and really concentrated. Immediately, the car began to lose power and slow down. As it crawled to a halt, the rear door was wrenched open and Professor Waters looked in at them.

'Quick!' he shouted. 'Get out!'

Mark and Lisa didn't need to be told twice. While Erica struggled to get out, Mark and Lisa ran to the Professor's car.

'How did you know Erica was a Watcher, Professor?' demanded Mark as Waters drove off.

'I didn't,' admitted Waters. 'But George had made me promise to look after you, so I followed you. While everything seemed alright I didn't interfere, but when I saw you two hammering on her car windows, I knew something had gone wrong.'

'Lucky for us!' sighed Mark. 'We have to get to the box straight away, Professor. We have to go through the doorway to save Uncle George!'

10 THE FINAL HOUR

MARK and Lisa stood in front of the open doorway. The tunnel glowed, dark, mysterious, frightening.

'Well, in we go,' said Mark. He took Lisa's hand and squeezed it gently, as much to reassure himself as to let his sister know that they would be alright.

'Be careful,' said Professor Waters.

Mark and Lisa took deep breaths and stepped into the tunnel. It appeared to go on for ever, winding and twisting. Ahead of them, they could see the light coming through the partly open door that led to Heritron. The nearer they got to the door, the slower they walked, watching and listening all the time. At last they were there.

Mark and Lisa peered out. They were looking onto a vast landing with a stairway that seemed to spiral endlessly upwards and downwards. A man in a soldier's uniform was on guard duty, his back to the doorway.

They scanned the area carefully. If only they could distract the soldier's attention for long enough, they could make a dash for the stairway.

Lisa tapped Mark on the shoulder, and then tapped her finger at her forehead. Mark understood: use their powers! They concentrated on a metal tray that a passing slave was carrying. As the tray fell to the floor with a loud crash, the guard went over to shout at the slave, and the children made their escape.

Instantly, Mark and Lisa scurried out of the tunnel and ran to the stairway. They hesitated, not knowing which way to go. Mark took the crystal from his pocket and they watched it glow, much brighter now.

'At least he's still alive,' Mark said, 'and pretty near, judging by the crystal. All we have to do is work out where.'

'Try moving,' suggested Lisa. 'Go in any direction and see what the crystal does.'

Mark took a few steps along the tunnel, and the crystal dimmed slightly. He retraced his steps and then went forward. This time the crystal glowed brighter.

'He's this way!' whispered Mark excitedly.

The twins hurried off along the tunnel, watching the crystal all the time.

Erica had finally arrived at the Janus Foundation. She was out of breath from running when she stumbled into Sir Derek Janus's office. She had tried to phone and tell him about Mark and Lisa, but every phone box had been out of order. Her car was useless and refused to start. So she had run all the way. She panted out her story about the Crystal Capsule and Anna and Ariana, while Janus gaped, shocked at what he was hearing.

'You mean, those two children, Mark and Lisa?'

'They are the Children of Heritron!' nodded Erica. 'I heard it all. I heard Anna tell them what to do: to go and rescue the Guardian!'

'So, by now they will have gone through the tunnel!' crowed Janus delightedly. 'The Takers will surely catch them! But what of the Crystal Capsule?'

'I left the bomb behind as you instructed,' smirked Erica. 'I took it with me as soon as I realised the children were taking me to the Capsule. Once I knew that Mark and Lisa were the children named in the legend, and that they would be going through to Heritron, then there was no further use for Anna.'

'Then Anna and Ariana will be destroyed!' cried Janus exultantly. 'The end of the rebels! Our triumph will be complete! Erica, you have done magnificently! This is our finest hour!' A sudden thought struck him, and he asked: 'Can you pinpoint exactly where the Crystal Capsule is?'

'Of course, sir,' replied Erica.

'Excellent. Come with me,' ordered Janus, and he led Erica to his office.

Janus entered the location of the Crystal Capsule into his holographic communicator.

'What are you doing, Sir Derek?' asked Erica, puzzled.

'I am about to gloat,' he replied, smiling broadly. 'These rebels are going to be destroyed. I want them to know it, and to know who it was that destroyed them.'

In the holographic communicator, the image of Anna and Ariana appeared.

'George? Mark? Lisa?' queried Anna. 'Is that you? I can't see you clearly.'

'But I can see you, Anna,' chuckled Janus mockingly.

'Who is this?' demanded Anna, her voice tense.

Janus moved a few switches and the picture became clearer. Anna could now see his face.

'There,' said Janus. 'We've never met, but you may have heard of me: Sir Derek Janus, Chief of the Watchers.'

The hardening of the expression on Anna's face told Janus that she had heard of him.

'I think you've already met my colleague,' he said. Anna peered at the image on her communicator, and now she could see Erica standing behind him.

'She left a little present behind when she called on you recently,' continued Janus. 'A bomb. I thought you'd like to know who it came from. It came from me.' He chuckled. 'This is the end, Anna. I calculate that you have just five more minutes. Five minutes of panic and fear while you try and work out where the bomb is. While you're doing that, I thought you'd also like to know what's happened to your friends. The Guardian has been captured. And as for the children – Mark and Lisa – by now the Catchers on Heritron will have them. It's all over, Anna. Finished!' He was still laughing when the image faded.

Ariana looked at Anna, horrified.

'A bomb?' she echoed.

'I knew that girl was not to be trusted!' scowled Anna. 'Luckily, she wasn't here long enough to have hidden it too far away. It will be close by. Close enough to hear it if we use our powers! Put our minds together!'

Anna and Ariana held hands, closed their eyes and concentrated, listening hard to every sound inside the Crystal Capsule. Gradually, they began to pick out a noise that they hadn't heard before: the sound of sand trickling out of a glass.

'That's it!' said Anna excitedly.

They began to search the shelves, trying to pinpoint the sound. Louder and louder it became, until there it was, coming from behind a row of books. Anna lifted the books away, and revealed a bomb in the shape of an hourglass.

Ariana watched as Anna began to use her powers to defuse the bomb. As the last grains of sand dropped through, Anna and Ariana held their breath, too scared to even breathe. Then everything was normal again, the same sounds as before, and the bomb was harmless.

Mark and Lisa had followed the crystal, watching it grow brighter and brighter as they made their way along the corridor. Now it was glowing as bright as any light bulb.

They passed a short flight of stairs and immediately the crystal began to fade once more.

'We've gone too far,' exclaimed Lisa. 'We must turn back.'

They retraced their steps, and, as they approached the stairway, the crystal glowed brighter again.

Warily, they climbed the stairs and pushed open the heavy door at the top. It swung open to reveal George trapped in a crystal cell, the keys to the box still on the leather thong round his neck.

They pulled the grille out and scrambled through into the room that held the crystal cell. George saw them and gestured frantically, shouting, but the crystal was too thick for them to hear what he was trying to tell them.

Mark and Lisa examined the surface of the enormous crystal. There was no door, no window, no break in the wall of crystal at all.

'This is impossible!' groaned Lisa.

'No it isn't,' said Mark determinedly. 'We can use our powers to break it open!'

'How?' asked Lisa. 'Everyone on Heritron has the power. They'd hardly make it so it could be broken by just anyone.'

'But we aren't just anyone,' insisted Mark. 'We are the Children of Heritron. We have stronger powers than anyone else. Uncle George said so. He said he'd never seen such strong powers. It must be something to do with us using them together because we're twins. I know we can do it. You just have to believe in it.'

'I don't know,' said Lisa doubtfully.

'Don't start doubting your power now!' Marked urged. 'The more we believe in it, the stronger we'll be. Now come on!'

Together, they placed their hands flat against the crystal wall of the cell and concentrated.

They felt the crystal wall grow warm, then tremble.

'It's working!' cried Mark excitedly.

There was the sound of a loud crack and the crystal shattered. George stepped out and hugged them both.

'Let's go!' he said.

George, Mark and Lisa hurried back along the corridors, until they reached the room that held the doorway to the tunnel back to Earth. The room was now filling up with Catchers all armed with their equipment, preparing to go through the tunnel in pursuit of slaves.

'There are too many of them,' groaned Mark. 'We'll never do it!'

'Yes we will,' urged George. 'We'll just have to make a run for it. It's only a short distance. Whatever happens, stick close together. Ready? Now!'

They dashed frantically towards the tunnel doorway. At first the Catchers were so startled, they froze with surprise. Then, almost as one, they turned on George and the children.

'Catch them!' yelled the Chief Catcher.

'Think of a storm,' ordered George, grasping Mark and Lisa by the hand.

Immediately, a storm gathered round them, offering protection from anything the Catchers could hurl in their direction.

Slowly, George and the children edged their way backwards and finally managed to struggle into the tunnel opening. George slammed the door shut and held it fast. Howling in anger, the Catchers tugged at the door, trying desperately to pull it open.

'Take the keys!' commanded George.

Mark took the keys from round George's neck, and, under George's direction, placed them one at a time in their correct designs in the door. As the last key went in, there was a click. George stepped back. The door was locked.

There was a rumbling sound and the tunnel began to vibrate.

'What's happening?' shouted Lisa.

'The tunnel's breaking up!' yelled George. 'Quick! We must get back before it's destroyed!'

Back in the workshop, Waters stood watching the box, a look of concern on his face as smoke began to pour out of it. He could hear a rumbling sound. It was getting louder and louder. Could it be the Catchers coming through?

Then his expression changed to one of relief and delight as Mark and Lisa ran out of the box, with George close behind. There was the dull sound of an explosion, and then a rush of smoke as the tunnel finally collapsed.

Waters watched in horror as the box began to disintegrate.

'What's happening?' he asked in horror as the box turned to rubble and dust.

'The final prophecy has been fulfilled,' said George. 'The door has been locked by the Children of Heritron and the fate of Heritron has been sealed for ever. The doorway has been destroyed.'

'But now there's no proof of what happened,' groaned Waters. 'Do you realise what this would have meant in scientific circles if we could have told the world. I – that is, *we* – would have been famous!'

'No one would have believed us!' said Lisa, gently.

'It's better this way, Professor, believe me,' sympathised George. 'It's all over.'

It was much later. George, Mark and Lisa stood with Anna and Ariana inside the Crystal Capsule.

'So, this is farewell,' said Anna sadly. 'We will never forget you, Children of Heritron, and what you have done for your world and ours.'

'Can't you stay here?' asked Lisa.

'No. We must return to Heritron,' said Anna. 'With the tunnel shut, the power of the Supreme Taker will be at an end, and the days of slavery will be over. We will rebuild Heritron as a better and fairer world.' Turning to George, she appealed: 'Will you come with us, George? There is much work to be done.'

George shook his head.

'This is my world, Anna,' he said. 'I belong here.'

'Will you ever come back?' asked Mark.

'Sadly, we cannot,' replied Anna. 'Already Heritron draws away. Our time is nigh. We must leave now.'

'We will think of you both, always,' said George.

They clasped hands in one last farewell, then Anna placed her hands on her communicator control. There was a momentary shimmering, and the Crystal Capsule and Anna and Ariana disappeared. George, Mark and Lisa were left standing among the ruins of the old derelict shop.

'It's sad to think we'll never see them again,' sighed Lisa.

'I know, but they have a world to rebuild,' said George.

'What about Sir Derek Janus and the Watchers?' asked Mark. 'What are we going to do about them?'

'Nothing,' answered George. 'Now the tunnel has gone for ever, they can never get back to Heritron. They're finished.'

'Won't they come after us?' asked Lisa, still a bit fearful.

'Not now they know you two are the Children of Heritron and that you have such great powers,' George reassured them. 'In fact, I think they'll be more worried that you'll look for them.'

George looked around the derelict shop and gave a wistful sigh. 'Come on, let's go home. Your mother will be back before us if we don't get a move on.'

They had barely arrived back at the house when Mark and Lisa's mother arrived to collect them. Mark and Lisa ran out to greet her.

'Am I happy to be here!' said their mother with a great sigh of relief. 'The things that have happened to me in the past week! The local shop ran out of bread. Your grandfather found fault with my cooking. Then I had a puncture on the way here.' She looked round at the park with a happy smile. 'I tell you, after the hectic time I've had, it'll be nice to have a quiet rest here, where nothing out of the ordinary ever happens.'

With that she took her suitcase out of the car and headed for the house. Behind her, George, Mark and Lisa exchanged looks that said very clearly: 'Where nothing out of the ordinary ever happens? Oh, really?!'

and All That

A Memorable History of England
comprising all the parts you can remember,
including 103 Good Things,
5 Bad Kings, and
2 Genuine Dates

By
WALTER CARRUTHERS SELLAR
Aegrot: Oxon.

and
ROBERT JULIAN YEATMAN
Failed M.A., *etc., Oxon.*

PENGUIN BOOKS
IN ASSOCIATION WITH METHUEN

Penguin Books Ltd, Harmondsworth, Middlesex, England
Penguin Books Australia Ltd, Ringwood, Victoria, Australia
Penguin Books Canada Ltd, 41 Steelcase Road West,
Markham, Ontario, Canada

—

First published by Methuen 1930
Published in Penguin Books 1960
Reprinted 1960, 1961, 1962, 1963, 1964, 1965, 1967, 1969, 1970,
1971, 1972, 1973, 1974

—

Made and printed in Great Britain
by Cox & Wyman Ltd,
London, Reading and Fakenham
Set in Monotype Plantin

DEDICATION
Absit Oman

COMPULSORY PREFACE

(*This Means You*)

HISTORIES have previously been written with the object of exalting their authors. The object of this History is to console the reader. *No other history does this.*

History is not what you thought. *It is what you can remember.* All other history defeats itself.

This is the only Memorable History of England, because all the History that you can remember is in this book, which is the result of years of research in golf-clubs, gun-rooms, green-rooms, etc.

For instance, two out of the four Dates originally included were eliminated at the last moment, a research done at the Eton and Harrow match having revealed that they are *not memorable.*

The Editors will be glad of further assistance towards the elimination, in future editions, of any similarly un-historical matter which, despite their vigilance, may have crept into the text.

They take this opportunity of acknowledging their inestimable debt to the mass of educated men and women of their race whose historical intuitions and opinions this work enshrines.

Also, to the Great British People without whose self-sacrificing determination to become top Nation there would have been no (memorable) history.

History is now at an end (see p. 123); this History is therefore final.

W. C. S.

R. J. Y.

PREFACE TO SECOND EDITION

A FIRST edition limited to one copy and printed on rice paper and bound in buck-boards and signed by one of the editors was sold to the other editor, who left it in a taxi somewhere between Piccadilly Circus and the Bodleian.

W. C. S.
R. J. Y.

ACKNOWLEDGEMENTS

THE Editors acknowledge their comparative indebtedness to the Editors of the *Historical Review*, *Bradshaw*, the *Lancet*, *La Vie Parisienne*, etc., in which none of the following chapters has appeared. Their thanks are also due to their wife, for not preparing the index wrong. There is no index.

PRESS OPINIONS

'This slim volume . . .' – *Bookworm*
'. . . We look forward keenly to the appearance of their last work.' – *Review of Reviews of Reviews*
'. . . vague . . .' – *Vague*

ERRATA

p. 11 *For* Middletoe *read* Mistletoe.
p. 17 *For* looked 4th *read* looked forth.
p. 50 *For* Pheasant *read* Peasant, throughout.
p. 52 *For* sausage *read* hostage.

Authors' Note

Several portions of this book have
appeared in *Punch*, and are
reprinted here by courtesy of
the Proprietors of
that paper.

CHAPTER I

Caesar Invades Britain

THE first date* in English History is 55 B.C., in which year Julius Caesar (the *memorable* Roman Emperor) landed, like all other successful invaders of these islands, at Thanet. This was in the Olden Days, when

Top nation

the Romans were top nation on account of their classical education, etc.

Julius Caesar advanced very energetically, throwing his cavalry several thousands of paces over the River Flumen; but the Ancient Britons, though all well over military age, painted themselves true blue, or *woad*, and fought as heroically under their dashing queen, Woadicea, as they did later in thin red lines under their good queen, Victoria.

*For the other date see Chapter 11, *William the Conqueror*

Julius Caesar was therefore compelled to invade Britain again the following year (54 B.C., not 56, owing to the peculiar Roman method of counting), and having defeated the Ancient Britons by unfair means, such as

Dawn of British heroism

battering-rams, tortoises, hippocausts, centipedes, axes, and bundles, set the memorable Latin sentence, 'Veni, Vidi, Vici', which the Romans, who were all very well educated, construed correctly.

The Britons, however, who of course still used the old pronunciation, understanding him to have called them 'Weeny, Weedy, and Weaky', lost heart and gave up the struggle, thinking that he had already divided them All into Three Parts.

Culture among the Ancient Britons

The Ancient Britons were by no means savages before the Conquest, and had already made great strides in civilization, e.g. they buried each other in long round wheelbarrows (agriculture) and burnt each other alive (religion) under the guidance of even older Britons called Druids or Eisteddfods, who worshipped the

Agriculture

Middletoe in the famous Druidical churchyard at Stoke Penge.

The Roman Conquest was, however, a *Good Thing*, since the Britons were only natives at that time.

The Roman Occupation

For some reason the Romans neglected to overrun the country with fire and the sword, though they had both of these; in fact, after the Conquest they did not mingle

Roman occupied

with the Britons at all, but lived a semi-detached life in villas. They occupied their time for two or three hundred years in building Roman roads and having Roman baths; this was called the Roman Occupation, and gave rise to the memorable Roman law, 'HE WHO BATHS FIRST BATHS FAST,' which was a Good Thing, and still is. The Roman roads ran absolutely straight in all directions and all led to Rome. The Romans also built towns wherever they were wanted, and, in addition, a wall between England and Scotland to keep out the savage Picts and Scots. This wall was the work of the memorable Roman Emperor Balbus and was thus called Hadrian's Wall. The Picts, or painted men,* were so called to distinguish them from the Britons. (See *supra, woad.*)

CHAPTER 2

Britain Conquered Again

THE withdrawal of the Roman legions to take part in Gibbon's Decline and Fall of the Roman Empire (due to a clamour among the Romans for pompous amusements such as bread and circumstances) left Britain defenceless and subjected Europe to that long succession of Waves of which History is chiefly composed. While the Roman Empire was overrun by waves not only of Ostrogoths, Vizigoths, and even Goths, but also of Vandals (who destroyed works of art) and Huns (who destroyed everything and everybody, including Goths, Ostrogoths, Vizigoths, and even Vandals), Britain was attacked by waves of Picts (and, of course, Scots) who had recently learnt how to climb the wall, and of Angles,

*e.g. The Black Watch, The Red Comyn, and Douglases of all colours.

Saxons, and Jutes who, landing at Thanet, soon over-ran the country with fire (and, of course, the sword).

Important Note

The Scots (originally Irish, but by now Scotch) were at this time inhabiting Ireland, having driven the Irish (Picts) out of Scotland; while the Picts (originally Scots) were now Irish (living in brackets) and *vice versa*. It is essential to keep these distinctions clearly in mind (and *verce visa*).

Humiliation of the Britons

The brutal Saxon invaders drove the Britons westward into Wales and compelled them to become Welsh; it is now considered doubtful whether this was a Good

(? or horse)

Thing. Memorable among the Saxon warriors were Hengist and his wife (? or horse), Horsa. Hengist made himself King in the South. Thus Hengist was the first English King and his wife (or horse), Horsa, the first

English Queen (or horse). The country was now almost entirely inhabited by Saxons and was therefore re-named England, and thus (naturally) soon became C. of E. This was a Good Thing, because previously the Saxons had worshipped some dreadful gods of their own called Monday, Tuesday, Wednesday, Thursday, Friday, and Saturday.

CHAPTER 3

The Conversion of England

NOTICING some fair-haired children in the slave market one morning, Pope Gregory, the memorable Pope, said (in Latin), 'What are those?' and on being

Angels?

told that they were Angels, made the memorable joke – '*Non Angli, sed Angeli*' ('*not* Angels, but *Anglicans*') and commanded one of his Saints called St Augustine to go and convert the rest.

The conversion of England was thus effected by the landing of St Augustine in Thanet and other places, which resulted in the country being overrun by a Wave

14

of Saints. Among these were St Ive, St Pancra, the great St Bernard (originator of the clerical collar), St Bee, St Ebb, St Neot (who invented whisky), St Kit and St Kin, and the Venomous Bead (author of *The Rosary*).

Wave of Sts

England was now divided into seven kingdoms and so ready were the English to become C. of E. that on one memorable occasion a whole Kingdom was easily converted by a sparrow.

Wave of Egg-Kings

Soon after this event Egg-Kings were found on the thrones of all these kingdoms, such as Eggberd, Eggbreth, Eggfroth, etc. None of them, however, succeeded in becoming memorable – except in so far as it is difficult to forget such names as Eggbirth, Eggbred, Eggbeard, Eggfish, etc. Nor is it even remembered by what kind of Eggdeath they perished.

CHAPTER 4

Britain Conquered Again

THE conversion of Britain was followed by a Wave of Danes, accompanied by their sisters or *Sagas*, and led by such memorable warriors as Harold Falsetooth and Magnus the Great, who, landing correctly in Thanet, overran the country from right to left, with fire.* After this the Danes invented a law called the Danelaw, which easily proved that since there was nobody else left alive there, all the right-hand part of England belonged to them. The Danish Conquest was, however, undoubtedly a *Good Thing*, because although it made the Danes top nation for a time it was the cause of Alfred the Cake (and in any case they were beaten utterly *in the end* by Nelson).

By this time the Saxons had all become very old like the Britons before them and were called *ealdormen*; when they had been defeated in a battle by the Danes they used to sing little songs to themselves such as the memorable fragment discovered in the Bodleian Library at Oxford:

Old-Saxon Fragment

Syng a song of Saxons
In the Wapentake of Rye
Four and twenty eaoldormen
Too eaold to die. . . .

Anon.

*And, according to certain obstinate historians, the Sword.

16

The Danes, on the other hand, wrote a very defiant kind of Epic poetry, e.g.:

Beoleopard
OR
The Witan's Whail

Whan Cnut Cyng the Witan wold enfeoff
Of infangthief and outfangthief
Wonderlich were they enwraged
And wordwar waged
Sware Cnut great scot and lot
Swingë wold ich this illbegotten lot.

Wroth was Cnut and wrothword spake.
Well wold he win at wopantake.
Fain wold he brakë frith and crackë heads
And than they shold worshippe his redes.

Swingéd Cnut Cyng with swung sword
Howléd Witanë hellë but hearkened his word
Murië sang Cnut Cyng
Outfangthief is Damgudthyng.

CHAPTER 5

Alfred the Cake

KING ALFRED was the first Good King, with the exception of Good King Wenceslas, who, though he looked 4th, really came first (it is not known, however, what King Wenceslas was King of). Alfred ought never to be confused with King Arthur, equally memorable but probably non-existent and therefore perhaps less important historically (unless he did exist).

There is a story that King Arthur once burnt some cakes belonging to Mrs Girth, a great lady of the time, at a place called Atheling. As, however, Alfred could not have been an Incendiary King *and* a Good King, we may dismiss the story as absurd, and in any case the event is supposed to have occurred in a marsh where the cakes would not have burnt properly. Cf. the famous lines of poetry about King Arthur and the cakes:

'Then slowly answered Alfred from the marsh – '
Arthur, Lord Tennyson.

CHAPTER 6

Exgalahad and the British Navy

KING ARTHUR invented Conferences because he was secretly a Weak King and liked to know what his memorable thousand and one Knights wanted to do next. As they were all parfitly jealous Knights he had to have the Memorable Round Table made to have the Conferences at, so that it was impossible to say which was top knight. He had a miraculous sword called Exgalahad with which he defeated the Danes in numerous battles. In this he was also much assisted by his marine inventions, including the water-clock and the British Navy. The latter invention occurred as follows.

Alfred noticed that the Danes had very long ships, so he built a great many more much longer ones, thus

cleverly founding the British Navy. From that time onwards foreigners, who, unlike the English, do not prefer
to fight against long odds, seldom attacked the British
Navy. Hence the important International Law called
the Rule Britannia, technically known as the Freedom
of the Seas.

Humiliation of the Danes

The English resisted the Danes heroically under Alfred,
never fighting except against heavy odds, till at the
memorable Peace of Wedmore Alfred compelled the
Danes, who were now (of course) beaten, to stop being
Danes and become English and therefore C. of E. and
get properly married.

For this purpose they were made to go back and start
again at Thanet, after which they were called in future
Thanes instead of Danes and were on our side and in
the right and very romantic.

CHAPTER 7

Lady Windermere. Age of Lake Dwellers

ALFRED had a very interesting wife called Lady
Windermere (The Lady of the Lake), who was always
clothed in the same white frock, and used to go bathing
with Sir Launcelot (also of the Lake) and was thus a
Bad Queen. It was also in King Arthur's time that the
Anglo-Saxon Chronicle was published: this was the first

English newspaper and had all the news about his victories, and Lady Windermere, and the Cakes, etc.

A Bad Queen

CHAPTER 8

Ethelread the Unready: A Weak King

ETHELREAD THE UNREADY was the first Weak King of England and was thus the cause of a fresh Wave of Danes.

He was called the Unready because he was never ready when the Danes were. Rather than wait for him the Danes used to fine him large sums called Danegeld, for not being ready. But though they were always ready, the Danes had very bad memories and often used to forget that they had been paid the Danegeld and come back for it almost before they had sailed away. By that time Ethelread was always unready again.

Finally, Ethelread was taken completely unawares by his own death and was succeeded by Canute.

CHAPTER 9

Canute, an Experimental King

THIS memorable monarch, having set out from Norway to collect some Danegeld, landed by mistake at Thanet, and thus became King.

Canute and the Waves

Canute began by being a Bad King on the advice of his Courtiers, who informed him (owing to a misunderstanding of the Rule Britannia) that the King of Eng-

A Bad King

land was entitled to sit on the sea without getting wet. But finding that they were wrong he gave up this policy and decided to take his own advice in future – thus originating the memorable proverb, 'Paddle your own Canute' – and became a Good King and C. of E., and ceased to be memorable. After Canute there were no more aquatic kings till William IV (see later, Creation of Piers).

Canute had two sons, Halfacanute and Partacanute, and two other offspring, Rathacanute and Hardlicanute,

whom, however, he would never acknowledge, denying to the last that he was their Fathacanute.

CHAPTER 10

Edward the Confessor

ON his death Canute's Kingdom was divided between two further sons, who had been previously overlooked, Aftercanute and Harold Harebrush. These were succeeded by Edward the Confessor. It was about this time that the memorable Mac Beth ('Ian Hay'), known as the Bane of Fife, murdered a number of his enemies, including Mac Duff, Lord Dunsinaney, Sleep, etc.

Edward the Confessor was with difficulty prevented from confessing to all these and many other crimes committed in his reign, as he was in the habit of confessing everything whether he had done it or not, and was thus a Weak King.

The Last English King

With Edward the Confessor perished the last English King (viz. Edward the Confessor), since he was succeeded by Waves of Norman Kings (French), Tudors (Welsh), Stuarts (Scottish), and Hanoverians (German), not to mention the memorable Dutch King-William-anmary.

TEST PAPER I

Up to the End of 1066

1. Which do you consider were the more alike, Caesar or Pompey, or *vice versa*? (Be brief.)

2. Discuss, in latin or gothic (*but not both*), whether the Northumbrian Bishops were more schismatical than the Cumbrian Abbots. (Be bright.)

3. Which came first, A.D. or B.C.? (Be careful.)

4. Has it never occurred to you that the Romans *counted backwards*? (Be honest.)

5. How angry would you be if it was suggested
   (1) That the XIth Chap. of the *Consolations of Boethius* was an interpolated palimpsest?
   (2) That an eisteddfod was an agricultural implement?

6. How would you have attempted to deal with
   (*a*) The Venomous Bead?
   (*b*) A Mabinogion or Wapentake? (Be quick.)

7. What would have happened if (*a*) Boadicea had been the daughter of Edward the Confessor? (*b*) Canute had succeeded in sitting on the waves?
   Does it matter?

8. Have you the faintest recollection of
   (1) Ethelbreth?
   (2) Athelthral?
   (3) Thruthelthrolth?
9. What *have* you the faintest recollection of?
10. Estimate the average age of
    (1) The Ancient Britons.
    (2) Ealdormen.
    (3) Old King Cole.
11. Why do you know nothing at all about
    (*a*) The Laws of Infangthief and Egg-seisin?
    (*b*) Saint Pancras?
12. Would you say that Ethelread the Unready was directly responsible for the French Revolution? If so, what *would* you say?

N.B. – Do not attempt to answer more than one question at a time.

CHAPTER II

William I: A Conquering King

IN the year 1066 occurred the other memorable date in English History, viz. *William the Conqueror, Ten Sixty-six*. This is also called *The Battle of Hastings*, and was when William I (1066) conquered England at the Battle of Senlac (*Ten Sixty-six*).

When William the Conqueror landed he lay down on the beach and swallowed two mouthfuls of sand. This was his first conquering action and was in the South; later he ravaged the North as well.

The Norman Conquest was a Good Thing, as from this time onwards England stopped being conquered and thus was able to become top nation.

First Conquering Action

Doomsday Book and the Forests

William next invented a system according to which everybody had to belong to somebody else, and everybody else to the King. This was called the Feutile System, and in order to prove that it was true he wrote a book called the *Doomsday Book*, which contained an inventory of all the Possessions of all his subjects; after reading the book through carefully William agreed with it and signed it, indicating to everybody that the Possessions mentioned in it were now his.

William the Conqueror (1066) is memorable for having loved an old stag as if it was his father, and was in general very fond of animals: he therefore made some very just and conquering laws about the Forests. One of these laws said that *all the forests and places which were not already Possessions belonged to the King* and that anyone found in them should *have his ears and legs cut off* — (these belonged to somebody else under the Feutile

System, anyway) – and (if this had not already been done) should have his *eyes put out with red-hot irons*; after this the offender was allowed to fly the country.

Another very conquering law made by William I said that everyone had to go to bed at eight o'clock. This was called the Curfew and was a Good Thing in the end since it was the cause of Gray's Energy in the country churchyard (at Stoke Penge).

Although in all these ways William the Conqueror (1066) was a very strong king he was eventually stumbled to death by a horse and was succeeded by his son Rufus.

CHAPTER 12

Rufus: A Ruddy King

THIS monarch was always very angry and red in the face and was therefore unpopular, so that his death was

A Good Thing

a Good Thing: it occurred in the following memorable way. Rufus was hunting one day in the New Forest, when William Tell (the memorable crackshot, inventor of Cross-bow puzzles) took unerring aim at a reddish apple, which had fallen on to the King's head, and shot him through the heart. Sir Isaac Walton, who happened to be present at the time, thereupon invented the Law of Gravity. Thus was the reign of Rufus brought to a Good End.

CHAPTER 13

Henry I: A Tragic King

HENRY I was famous for his handwriting and was therefore generally called Henry Beau-geste. He was extremely fond of his son William, who was, however, drowned in the White City. Henry tried to console himself for his loss by eating a surfeit of palfreys. This was a Bad Thing since he died of it and *never smiled again*.

CHAPTER 14

The Dreadful Story of Stephen and his Aunt Matilda (or Maud)

THE moment Stephen came to the throne it was realized that he was a mistake and had been christened wrong; thus everything was thrown into confusion.

Stephen himself felt quite uncalled for, and even his Aunt Matilda was able to take him in when she began announcing that she was the real King. Stephen, however, soon discovered that she had been malchristened, too, and was unable to say for certain whether her name was Matilda or Maud.

After this Stephen and Matilda (or Maud) spent the reign escaping from each other over the snow in night-gowns while 'God and His Angels slept'.

Lax State of Affairs

Taking advantage of this lax state of affairs, the Barons built a surfeit of romantic castles, into which they lured everybody and then put them to the torture; nor is it recorded that the Sword was once sheathed right to the bottom, during the whole of this dreadful reign. Hence the memorable greeting so common among the Barons of the time – 'Merrie Englande!'

CHAPTER 15

Henry II: A Just King

HENRY II was a great Lawgiver, and it was he who laid down the great Legal Principle that everything is either legal or (preferably) illegal.

He also made another very just arrangement about trials:

Before Henry II's time there were two kinds of legal trial, (*a*) the Ideal and (*b*) the Combat. The Ideal form of trial consisted in making a man plunge his head in boiling ploughshares, in order to see whether he had committed a crime or not. According to Henry's reformed system a man was tried first by a jury of his equals and only had to plunge his head into the ploughshares afterwards (in order to confirm the jury's opinion that he had committed the crime). This was obviously a much *Better Thing*.

The Combat was a system by which in civil cases the litigants decided their dispute by mortal combat, after which the defeated party was allowed to fly the country. But Henry altered all this and declared that a Grand Jury must decide first what the parties were fighting about: a reform which naturally gave rise to grave discontent among the Barons, who believed in the Combat, the whole Combat and nothing but the Combat.

Thomas à Belloc

It was at this time that Thomas à Belloc, the great religious leader, claimed that clergymen, whatever crimes they might commit, could not be punished at all; this privilege, which was for some reason known as Benefit of Clergy, was in full accord with the devout spirit of the age. Henry II, however, exclaimed to some of his Knights one day, 'Who will rid me of this Chesterton beast?' Whereupon the Knights pursued Belloc and murdered him in the organ at Canterbury Cathedral. Belloc was therefore made a Saint and the Knights came to be called the Canterbury Pilgrims.

29

Shortly afterwards Henry died of despair on receiving news that his sons were all revolting.

CHAPTER 16

The Age of Piety

THE Chapters between William I (1066) and the Tudors (Henry VIII, etc.) are always called the *Middle Ages*, on account of their coming at the beginning; this was also *The Age of Piety*, since Religious fervour was then at its height, people being (1) burnt alive with faggots (The Steak), (2) bricked up in the walls of Convents (Religious Foundations), and (3) tortured in dungeons (The Confessional).

All this was not only pious but a Good Thing, as many of the people who were burnt, bricked, tortured, etc., became quite otherworldly.

Nowadays people are not so pious, even sinners being denied the benefits of fervent Religion.

CHAPTER 17

Richard I: A Wild King

RICHARD I was a hairy King with a Lion's Heart; he went roaring about the Desert making ferocious attacks on the Saladins and the Paladins, and was thus a very romantic King. Whenever he returned to England he always set out again immediately for the Mediterranean and was therefore known as Richard Gare de Lyon. He had a sword of enormous dimensions with which he used to practise cutting iron bars and anvils in half, whereas the Saladins had very sharp swords which were

A Wild King

only useful for cutting cushions in half. In spite of which the Crusaders under Richard never got Jerusalem back; this was undoubtedly due to the treacherous behaviour of the Saladins, who used to fire on the Red Cross which the Crusaders wore on their chests in battle.

The Story of Blondin

Richard is also famous for having a minstrel boy (or Touralour) called Blondin who searched for him under the walls of all the dungeons in Europe. This was when Richard had been caught by the blind King of Bohemia during a game of Blind King's Bluff and sold to the Holy Roman Terror. Blondin eventually found him by singing the memorable song (or 'touralay') called *O Richard et mon Droit* ('Are you right, there, Richard?') which Richard himself had composed. Richard roared the chorus so that Blondin knew which dungeon he was in, and thus the King easily escaped and returned to the Crusades, where he died soon after of a surfeit of Saladins, and was therefore known in the East as Richard Cœur de Laitue.

CHAPTER 18

John: An Awful King

WHEN John came to the throne he lost his temper and flung himself on the floor, foaming at the mouth and biting the rushes. He was thus a Bad King. Indeed, he had begun badly as a Bad Prince, having attempted to answer the Irish Question* by pulling the beards of the aged Irish chiefs, which was a Bad Thing and the wrong answer.

Prince Arthur – A Tragedy in Little

John had a little nephew called Little Arthur, who was writing a little History of England in quite a small dungeon, and whose little blue eyes John had ordered to be put out with some weeny red-hot irons. The gaoler Hubert, however, who was a Good Man, wept so much that he put out the red-hot irons instead. John was therefore compelled to do the little deed himself with a large, smallish knife, thus becoming the first memorable wicked uncle.

*N.B. – The Irish Question at this time consisted of:
  (1) Some Norman Barons, who lived in a Pail (near Dublin),
  (2) The natives and Irish Chieftains, who were beyond the Pail, living in bogs, beards, etc.

John was so bad that the Pope decided to put the whole country under an Interdict, i.e. he gave orders that no one was to be born or die or marry (except in Church porches). But John was still not cured of his Badness; so the Pope sent a Bull to England to excommunicate John himself. In spite of the King's efforts to prevent it the Bull succeeded in landing and gave orders that John himself was not to be born or marry or die (except in Church porches); that no one was to obey him or stand him a drink or tell him the right time or the answer to the Irish Question or anything nice. So at last John gave way and he and his subjects began once more to be born and to marry and to die, etc. etc.

CHAPTER 19

Magna Charter

THERE also happened in this reign the memorable Charta, known as Magna Charter on account of the Latin *Magna* (great) and Charter (a Charter); this was the first of the famous Chartas and Gartas of the Realm and was invented by the Barons on a desert island in the Thames called Ganymede. By congregating there, armed to the teeth, the Barons compelled John to sign the Magna Charter, which said:

1. That no one was to be put to death, save for some reason – (except the Common People).

2. That everyone should be free – (except the Common People).
3. That everything should be of the same weight and measure throughout the Realm – (except the Common People).
4. That the Courts should be stationary, instead of following a very tiresome medieval official known as the *King's Person* all over the country.
5. That 'no person should be fined to his utter ruin' – (except the King's Person).
6. That the Barons should not be tried except by a special jury of other Barons who would understand.

Magna Charter was therefore the chief cause of Democracy in England, and thus a *Good Thing* for everyone (except the Common People).

Utter Incompetence

After this King John hadn't a leg to stand on and was therefore known as 'John Lackshanks'.

Final Acts of Misgovernment

John finally demonstrated his utter incompetence by losing the Crown and all his clothes in the wash and then dying of a surfeit of peaches and no cider; thus his awful reign came to an end.

CHAPTER 20

Robin Hood and his Merrie Men

ABOUT this time the memorable hero Robin Hood flourished in a romantic manner. Having been unjustly accused by two policemen in Richmond Park, he was condemned to be an outdoor and went and lived with a maid who was called Marion, and a band of Merrie Men, in Greenwood Forest, near Sherborne. Amongst his Merrie Men were Will Scarlet (*The Scarlet Pimpernel*), Black Beauty, White Melville, Little Red Riding Hood (probably an outdaughter of his), and the famous Friar Puck who used to sit in a cowslip and suck bees, thus becoming so fat that he declared he could put his girdle round the Earth.

Robin Hood was a miraculous shot with the longbow and it is said that he could split a hare at 400 paces and a Sheriff at 800. He therefore spent his time blowing a horn and shooting at the Sheriff of Nottingham (who was an outwit). He always used to sound his horn first, particularly when shooting round a corner; this showed his sportsmanship and also enabled him to shoot the Sheriff running, which was more difficult.

Robin Hood was also very good at socialism and often took money away from rich clergymen and gave it to the poor, who loved him for his generosity. He died very romantically. Having taken some medicine supplied by his Wicked Aunt and feeling his strength going, he blew a dying blast on his horn and with his dying

Sheriff running . . . more difficult

breath fired a last shot out of his bedroom window, and *hit the Sheriff of Nottingham again.*

CHAPTER 21

Henry III: A Nondescript King

HENRY III was a confused kind of King and is only memorable for having seized all the money in the Mint, imprisoned himself in the Tower of London and, finally, flung himself into the Bosom of the Pope.

While he was in the Tower, Henry III wrote a letter to the nation saying that he was a Good Thing. This so confused the Londoners that they armed themselves with staves, jerkins, etc., and massacred the Jews in the City. Later, when he was in the Pope's Bosom, Henry further confused the People by presenting all the Bonifaces of the Church to Italians. And the whole reign was rapidly becoming less and less memorable when one of the Barons called Simon de Montfort saved the situation by announcing that he had a memorable Idea.

Simon de Montfort's Good Idea

Simon de Montfort's Idea was to make the Parliament more Representative by inviting one or two vergers, or vergesses, to come from every parish, thus causing the only Good Parliament in History.

The Barons

Simon de Montfort, though only a Frenchman, was thus a Good Thing, and is very notable as being the only good Baron in history. The other Barons were, of course, all wicked Barons. They had, however, many important duties under the Banorial system. These were:

1. To be armed to the teeth.
2. To extract from the Villein* Saccage and Soccage, tollage and tallage, pillage and ullage, and, in extreme cases, all

To extract from *The Villein*

Villein: medieval term for agricultural labourer, usually suffering from scurvy, Black Death, etc.

37

other banorial amenities such as umbrage and porrage. (These may be collectively defined as the banorial rites of carnage and wreckage.)

3. To hasten the King's death, deposition, insanity, etc., and make quite sure that there were always at least three false claimants to the throne.

4. To resent the Attitude of the Church. (The Barons were secretly jealous of the Church, which they accused of encroaching on their rites – see p. 30, *Age of Piety*.)

5. To keep up the Middle Ages.

Note

In order to clear up the general confusion of the period it is customary to give at this point a genealogical table of the Kings (and even some Queens) of England. As these tables are themselves somewhat confusing, the one on the page opposite has been to a certain extent *rationalized*, and will, the Editors hope, prove to be exceptionally memorable.

TEST PAPER II

Up to the End of Henry III

*1. Give the dates of at least two of the following:
    (1) William the Conqueror.
    (2) 1066.

*2. What is a Plantagenet? Do you agree?

*3. Trace by means of graphs, etc.,
    (1) The incidence of scurvy in the Chiltern Hundreds during the reign of Rufus.
    (2) The Bosom of the Pope.
    (Squared paper, compasses, etc., may be used.)

Julius Caesar = Cymbaline

Balbus = Boadicea

Alfred (Arthur) = Lady Windermere
(The Lady of the Lake)

John of Gaunt = (1) Lady Godiva
(2) Margaret of Angoulême
(3) Joan of Arc
(4) The Infanta
(5) The Maria Theresa
(6) Ann of Geierstein
(7) etc.
(8) etc. etc.

Richard I
Richard II
Richard III

James I
James II
Charles I
Charles II
George I
George II
George III
George IV

Henry I o.s.p.*
Henry II
Henry III
Henry IV (Part I)
Henry V
Henry VI
Henry VII
Henry VIII

Edward the Confessor = The Lady of Shalott

William I
William II
Williamanmary
William IV

Broody Mary
Elizabeth
Anne

Edward I
Edward II
Edward III
Edward IV
Edward V
Edward VI
Edward VII

Victoria

Carried forward:— Ole King Cole
Stephen
John o.s.p.†
Henry IV (Part II)

* obiit surfeiti palfreyorum (see p. 27)   † peaches

E. & O. E.

*4. Expostulate (chiefly) on
   (*a*) The Curfew.
   (*b*) Gray's Energy in the Country Churchyard.
*5. Estimate the size of
   (1) Little Arthur.
   (2) Friar Puck.
   (3) Magna Charta.
  6. Fill in the names of at least some of the following:
   (1) —————————.
   (2) —————————.
   (3) Simon de Montfort.
  7. King John had no redeeming features. (Illustrate.)
  8. Arrange in this order:
   (1) Henry I.
   (2) Henry II.
   (3) Henry III.
   (Do not attempt to answer more than once.)
*9. (*a*) How far did the Lords Repellent drive Henry III
       into the arms of Pedro the Cruel? (Protractors may
       not be used.)
   (*b*) Matilda or Maud? (Write on one side of the paper
       only.)
*10. How would you dispose of:
   (*a*) A Papal Bull?
   (*b*) Your nephews?
   (*c*) Your mother? (Be brutal.)
*11. Which would you rather be:
   (1) The Sheriff of Nottingham?
   (2) A Weak King?
   (3) Put to the Sword?

  *N.B. – Candidates over thirty need not attempt questions
10, 2, 5, 3, 4, 11, 9, or 1.

CHAPTER 22

Edward I: A Strong King

LONG before Henry III had died (of a surfeit of Barons, Bonifaces, etc.) Edward I had taken advantage of the general confusion and of the death of Simon de Montfort (probably of a surfeit of Vergers) to become King before his reign had begun.

Edward I was thus a strong King, and one of the first

Sat on it himself

things he did was to make a strong arrangement about the Law Courts. Hitherto there had been a number of Benches there, on all of which a confused official called the Justinian had tried to sit. Edward had them all amalgamated into one large Bench called the King's Bench, and sat on it himself.

Edward I, who had already (in his Saladin days) piously decimated several thousand Turks at Nazareth, now felt so strong that he decided to Hammer the Scots, who accordingly now come right into History.

The childless Scotch King Alexander the Great had trotted over a cliff and was thus dead; so the Scots asked Edward to tell them who was King of Scotland,

and Edward said that a Balliol man ought to be. Delighted with this decision the Scots crossed the Border and ravaged Cumberland with savage ferocity; in reply

Malleus Scotorum

to which Edward also crossed the Border and, carrying off the Sacred Scone of Scotland on which the Scottish Kings had been crowned for centuries, buried it with great solemnity in Westminster Abbey.

This was, of course, a Good Thing for the Scots because it was the cause of William the Wallace (not to be confused with Robert Bruce), who immediately

defeated the English at Cambuskenneth (Scotch for Stirling) and invaded England with ferocious savagery.

42

In answer to this Edward captured the Bruce and had him horribly executed with savage ferocity. Soon after, Edward died of suffocation at a place called Burrow-in-the-Sands and was succeeded by his worthless son Edward II.

CHAPTER 23

Edward II: A Worthless King

EDWARD II had a wave of favourites or hangers-on at Court, of whom the worst were the Suspenders and the Peers Gaveston. There were two memorable Suspenders, the Old Suspender and the Young Suspender,

and they were Edward's reply to the continual applications of the Barons for a confirmation of all the charters and garters of the Realm. But even Edward II's worthless character cannot alone explain.

The Scots were now under the leadership of the Bruce (not to be confused with the Wallace), who, doubtful whether he had slain the Red Comyn or not, armed

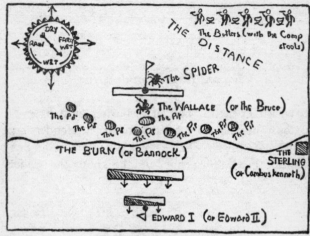

THE BANNOCKBURN
(or Flodden)

himself with an enormous spider and marched against the English, determined if possible to win back the Great Scone by beating the English three times running.

The fact that the English were defeated has so confused Historians that many false theories are prevalent about the Bannockburn Campaign. What actually happened is quite clear from the sketch map shown above.

44

The causes of the English defeat were all unfair and were:

1. *The Pits.* Every time the Wallace saw some English Knights charging at him he quickly dug one of these unnatural hazards into which the English Knights, who had been taught to ride straight, galloped with flying colours.
2. *Superior numbers of the English* (four to one). Accustomed to fight against heavy odds the English were uneasy, and when the Scots were unexpectedly reinforced by a large body of butlers with camp stools the English soldiers mistook them for a fresh army of Englishmen and retreated in disgust.
3. *Foul riding by Scottish Knights.* This was typified even before the battle during an exhibition combat between the Bruce and the English Champion, Baron Henry le Bohunk, when Bruce, mounted on a Shetland pony, galloped underneath the Baron and, coming up unexpectedly on the blind side, struck him a foul blow behind and maced him up for life.

Memorable Screams of Edward II

Edward II was so weak that he kept banishing his favourites and then unbanishing them again. The Barons therefore became so impatient that they deposed Edward without even waiting to arrange for any false claimants to the throne. Thus Edward III became King.

Shortly afterwards HORRIBLE SCREAMS were heard issuing from the Berkeley where Edward II was imprisoned and the next day he was horribly dead. But since not even the Barons would confess to having horribly murdered him, it is just possible that Edward had merely been dying of a surfeit in the ordinary way.

CHAPTER 24

Edward III: A Romantic King

EDWARD III had a very romantic reign which he began by confining his mother in a stronghold for the rest of her life, and inventing a law called the Gallic Law according to which he was King of France, and could therefore make war on it whenever he felt inclined.

In order to placate Edward, the French King sent him a box of new tennis balls. When the parcel was opened the Prince of Wales, who was present, mottoed to himself memorably (in Bohemian) *'Ich Dien'*, which means 'My serve', and immediately invaded France with an army of archers. This prince was the memorable All-Black Prince, and the war was called the Hundred Years' War, because the troops signed on for a hundred years or the duration.

The Battle of Cresy

This decisive battle of the world was fought during a total eclipçe of the sun and naturally ended in a complete victory for the All-Black Prince, who very romantically 'won his Spurs'* by slaughtering one-third of the French nobility.

---

*His father the King had betted him a pair of hotspurs that he could not do this.

46

Edward III then laid siege to Calais in order to be ready to return to England if necessary, and on the capitulation of the town ordered the six richest citizens to come forth with halters round their necks and wearing only their shorts, and to surrender all the keys in the city. The inhabitants therefore at once appointed the six chief burglars of Calais and Edward agreed with this, romantically commanding that they should be put to death as soon as they came in. His Queen, however, pointed out what a much more romantic thing it would be to pardon them and make them barons in the Exchequer. Edward therefore pardoned them in spite of his private feelings that the original plan was more romantic still.

After this Edward had all the wool in England kept in a stable at Calais instead of in a sack in the House of Commons; this was a Bad Thing, as it was the beginning of Political Economy.

Wyclif and the Dullards

During this reign the memorable preacher Wyclif collected together a curious set of men known as the Lollards or Dullards, because they insisted on walking about with their tongues hanging out and because they were so stupid that they could not do the Bible in Latin and demanded that everyone should be allowed to use an English translation. They were thus heretics and were accordingly unpopular with the top men in the

Church who were very good at Latin and who liked to see some Dullards burnt before every meal. Hence the

memorable grace '*De Heretico Comburendo, Amen*', known as the Pilgrim's Grace.

Royal Tact

Edward III had very good manners. One day at a royal dance he noticed some men-about-court mocking a lady whose garter had come off, whereupon to put her at her

ease he stopped the dance and made the memorable epitaph: '*Honi soie qui mal y pense*' ('Honey, your silk stocking's hanging down') and having replaced the garter with a romantic gesture gave the ill-mannered courtiers the Order of the Bath. (This was an extreme form of torture in the Middle Ages.)

CHAPTER 25

Richard II: An Unbalanced King

RICHARD II was only a boy at his accession: one day, however, suspecting that he was now twenty-one, he asked his uncle and, on learning that he was, mounted

Got off the throne

the throne himself and tried first being a Good King and then being a Bad King, without enjoying either very much: then, being told that he was unbalanced, he got off the throne again in despair, exclaiming gloomily: 'For God's sake let me sit on the ground and tell bad stories about cabbages and things.' Whereupon his cousin Lancaster (spelt Bolingbroke) quickly mounted the throne and said he was Henry IV Part I.

Richard was thus abdicated and was led to the Tower and subsequently to Pontefract Castle where he died of mysterious circumstances, probably a surfeit of Pumfreys (spelt Pontefracts).

APPENDIX

The Pheasants Revolt

They did this in several reigns under such memorable leaders as Black Kat, Straw Hat, John Bull, and What Tyler.

I. Objects:

   (a) to obtain a free pardon for having revolted.

   (b) to find out which was the gentleman when Adam delved and Eve span. (The answer was, of course, Adam, but the mystics of the Church had concealed this dangerous knowledge.)

   (c) to find out who was King and which of them was the Leader of the Rebellion.

   (d) to abolish the Villein.

The Pheasants' Revolts were therefore purely educational movements and were thus easily suppressed.

II. How Quelled:

   (a) the Pheasants were met at Smithfield by the King who

   (b) riding forward alone on a white horse answered object (c) by announcing (I) 'I am your King', and (II) 'I will be your leader'.

(c) the real leader was then slain quickly by one of the Barons.

(d) a free pardon was granted to the Pheasants [see object (a)].

(e) all were then put to death on the ground that they were Villeins [see object (d)].

These Revolts were thus clearly romantic episodes, and a Good Thing, and the clergy were enabled to prevent the pheasants finding out the answer to object (b).

CHAPTER 26

Henry IV: A Split King

WHEN Henry IV Part I came to the throne the Barons immediately flung their gloves on the floor in order to prove

1. That Richard II was not yet dead
2. That Henry had murdered him.

Henry very gallantly replied to this challenge by exhibiting Richard II's head in St Paul's Cathedral, thus proving that he was innocent. Finding, however, that he was not memorable, he very patriotically abdicated in favour of Henry IV Part II.

Renewed Educational Ferment

Even Henry IV Part II, however, is only memorable for having passed some interesting laws against his *Old Retainers*, i.e. butlers and sutlers, who had irritated him by demanding *Liveries*, requiring too much *Maintenance*, etc. He also captured the Scottish Prince James and, while keeping him as a sausage, had him carefully educated for nineteen years; finding, however, that James was still Scotch, Henry IV Part II lost interest in education and died.

CHAPTER 27

Henry V: An Ideal King

ON the death of Henry IV Part II, his son, Prince Hal, who had won all English hearts by his youthful pranks – (such as trying on the crown while his father lay dying, and hitting a very old man called Judge Gascoigne) –

determined to justify public expectation by becoming the *Ideal English King*. He therefore decided on an immediate appearance in the Hundred Years' War, making a declaration that all the treaties with France were to be regarded as dull and void.

Conditions in France were favourable to Henry since the French King, being mad, had entrusted the government of the country to a dolphin and the command of the army to an elderly constable. After capturing some breeches at Harfleur (more than once) by the original expedients of disguising his friends as imitation tigers, stiffening their sinews, etc., Henry was held up on the road to Calais by the constable, whom he defeated at the utterly memorable battle of AGINCOURT (French POICTIERS). He then displaced the dolphin as ruler of Anjou, Menjou, Poilou, Maine, Touraine, Againe, and Againe, and realizing that he was now too famous to live long expired at the ideal moment.

CHAPTER 28

Henry VI: A Very Small King

THE next King, Henry VI, was only one year old and was thus rather a Weak King; indeed the Barons declared that he was quite numb and vague. When he

A Weak King

53

grew up, however, he was such a Good Man that he was considered a Saint, or alternatively (especially by the Barons) an imbecile.

Joan of Ark

During this reign the Hundred Years' War was brought to an end by *Joan of Ark*, a French descendant of Noah who after hearing Angel voices singing *Do Ré Mi* became inspired, thus unfairly defeating the English in several battles. Indeed, she might even have made France top nation if the Church had not decided that she would make an exceptionally memorable martyr. Thus Joan of Ark was a Good Thing in the end and is now the only memorable French saint.

The Wars of the Roses

Noticing suddenly that the Middle Ages were coming to an end, the Barons now made a stupendous effort to revive the old Feudal amenities of Sackage, Carnage, and Wreckage and so stave off the Tudors for a time. They achieved this by a very clever plan, known as the *Wars of the Roses* (because the Barons all picked different coloured roses in order to see which side they were on).

Warwick the Kingmaker

One of the rules in the Wars of the Roses was that nobody was ever really King but that Edmund Mortimer really ought to be: any Baron who wished to be considered King was allowed to apply at Warwick the Kingmaker's, where he was made to fill up a form, answering the following questions:

1. Are you a good plain crook?
2. Are you Edmund Mortimer? If not, have you got him?
3. Have you ever been King before? If so, state how many times; also whether deposed, beheaded, or died of surfeit.
4. Are you insane? If so, state whether permanently or only temporarily.
5. Are you prepared to marry Margaret of Angoulme? If Isabella of Hainault preferred, give reasons. (Candidates are advised not to attempt both ladies.)
6. Have you had the Black Death?
7. What have you done with your mother? (If *Nun*, write *None*.)
8. Do you intend to be I (*a*) a Good King.
   (*b*) a Bad King.
   (*c*) a Weak King.
   II (*a*) a Good Man.
   (*b*) a Bad Man.
   (Candidates must not attempt more than one in each section.)
9. How do you propose to die? (Write your answer in BLOCK CAPITALS.)

CHAPTER 29

Cause of the Tudors

DURING the Wars of the Roses the Kings became less and less memorable (sometimes even getting in the wrong order) until at last one of them was nothing but

55

some little princes smothered in the Tower, and another, finding that his name was Clarence, had himself drowned in a spot of Malmsey wine; while the last of all even attempted to give his Kingdom to a horse. It was therefore decided, since the Stuarts were not ready yet, to have some Welsh Kings called Tudors (on account of their descent from Owen Glendower) who, it was hoped, would be more memorable.

Finding that his name
was Clarence

The first of these Welsh Kings was Henry VII, who defeated all other Kings at the Battle of Boswell Field and took away their roses. After the battle the crown was found hanging up in a hawthorn tree on top of a hill. This is memorable as being the only occasion on which the crown has been found after a battle hanging up in a hawthorn tree on top of a hill.

Henry VII's Statecraft

Henry VII was a miser and very good at statecraft; he invented some extremely clever policies such as the one called Morton's Fork. This was an enormous prong with which his minister Morton visited the rich citizens (or burghlers as they were called). If the citizen said he was poor, Morton drove his Fork in a certain distance and promised not to take it out until the citizen paid a

A certain distance

large sum of money to the King. As soon as this was forthcoming Morton dismissed him, at the same time shouting 'Fork Out' so that Henry would know the statecraft had been successful. If the burghler said he was quite rich Morton did the same thing: it was thus a very clever policy and always succeeded except when Morton put the Fork in too far.

CHAPTER 30

Lambert Simnel and Perkin Warbeck

ENGLISH History has always been subject to Waves of Pretenders. These have usually come in small waves of about two – an Old Pretender and a Young Pretender, their object being to sow dissension in the realm, and if possible to confuse the Royal issue by pretending to be heirs to the throne.

Two Pretenders who now arose were Lambert Simnel and Perkin Warbeck, and they succeeded in confusing the issue absolutely by being so similar that some historians suggest they were really the same person (i.e. the Earl of Warbeck).

Lambert Simnel (the Young Pretender) was really (probably) himself, but cleverly pretended to be the Earl of Warbeck. Henry VII therefore ordered him to be led through the streets of London to prove that he really was.

Perkin Warbeck (the Older and more confusing Pretender) insisted that he was himself, thus causing complete dissension till Henry VII had him led through the streets of London to prove that he was really Lambert Simnel.

The punishment of these memorable Pretenders was justly similar, since Perkin Warmnel was compelled to become a blot on the King's skitchen, while Perbeck was made an escullion. Wimneck, however, subsequently began pretending again. This time he pretended that he had been smothered in early youth and burled under a stair-rod while pretending to be one of the Little Princes in the Tower. In order to prove that he had not been murdered before, Henry was reluctantly compelled to have him really executed.

Punishment of Lamnel
(or Wermkin)

Even after his execution many people believed that he was only pretending to have been beheaded, while others declared that it was not Warmneck at all but Lamkin, and that Permnel had been dead all the time really, like Queen Anne.

Poyning's Law

Henry VII was very good at answering the Irish Question, and made a Law called Poyning's Law by which the Irish could have a Parliament of their own, but the English were to pass all the Acts in it. This was obviously a very Good Thing.

Age of Daring Discoveries

The reign of Henry VII marks the end of the Middle Ages. These were succeeded by an age of daring discoveries, such as when Caprornicus observed the Moon while searching the skies with a telescope, thus causing the rotation of the Earth, crops, etc. Emboldened by this, Caprornicus began openly discussing the topic of capricorns, for which he was unanimously put to death.

The greatest of these discoverers, however, was St Christophus Columba, the utterly memorable American, who, with the assistance of the intrepid adventurers John and Sebastian Robot, discovered how to make an egg stand on its wrong end. (Modern History is generally dated from this event.)

TEST PAPER III

Up to the End of Henry VII

1. Contract, Expand, and Explode
   (*a*) The Charters and Garters of the Realm.
   (*b*) The Old Suspender.
2. How did any *one* of the following differ from any one of the other?
   (1) Henry IV Part I.
   (2) Henry IV Part II.
3. 'The end of the closing of the 2nd stage of the Treaty of Bretigny marks the opening of a new phase in the 1st stage of the termination of the Hundred Years' War.' (Confute.)
4. 'Know ye not Agincourt?' (Confess.)
5. 'Uneasy lies the head that wears a Throne.'
   (*a*) Suggest remedies, or
   (*b*) Imitate the action of a Tiger.
6. Intone interminably (but inaudibly)
         i. The Pilgrims' Grace.
        ii. 'Cuccu'.

7. Do not draw a skotch-map of the Battle of Bannock-burn, but write not more than three lines on the advantages and disadvantages of the inductive historical method with special relation to ecclesiastical litigation in the earlier Lancastrian epochs.
8. How would you confuse
   (1) The Wars of the Roses?
   (2) Lamnel Simkin and Percy Warmneck?
   (3) The Royal issue?
9. Why do you picture John of Gaunt as a rather emaciated grandee?
10. Describe in excessive detail
    (a) The advantages of the Black Death.
    (b) The fate of the Duke of Clarence.
    (c) A Surfeit.

N.B. – Candidates should write on at least one side of the paper.

CHAPTER 31

Bluff King Hal

HENRY VIII was a strong King with a very strong sense of humour and VIII wives, memorable amongst whom were Katherine the Arrogant, Anne of Cloves, Lady Jane Austin, and Anne Hathaway. His beard was, however, red.

In his youth Henry was fond of playing tennis and after his accession is believed never to have lost a set. He also invented a game called '*Bluff King Hal*' which he invited his ministers to play with him. The players were blindfolded and knelt down with their heads on a block of wood; they then guessed whom the King would marry next.

Cardinal Wolsey, the memorable homespun statesman and inventor of the Wolsack, played this game with Henry and won. But his successor, Cromwell (*not to be confused with Cromwell*), after winning on points, was disqualified by the King (who always acted as umpire), and lost.

In the opinion of Shakespeare (the memorable playwriter and Top Poet) his unexpected defeat was due to his failure to fling away ambition.

The Restoration

Henry wanted the Pope to give him a divorce from his first wife, Katherine. He wanted this because

(*a*) she was Arrogant.
(*b*) he had married her a very long time ago.
(*c*) when she had a baby it turned out to be Broody Mary, and Henry wanted a boy.
(*d*) he thought it would be a Good Thing.

The Pope, however, refused, and seceded with all his

followers from the Church of England. This was called the Restoration.

Henry's Plan Fails

Curiously enough Henry had all the time had an idea about a new wife for himself called Anne, who, he thought, looked as if she would be sure to have a son. So when the Divorce was all over (or nearly) he married her; but he was wrong about Anne, because she had a girl too, in a way (see Elizabeth).

After this Henry was afraid his reign would not be long enough for any more divorces, so he gave them up and executed his wives instead.* He also got less interested in his wives and gave himself up to Diplomacy, spending a great deal of his time playing tennis, etc., with the young King of France in a field called the Field of the Crock of Gold.

End of Wolsey

Cardinal Wolsey, although (as is well known) he had not thought to shed a tear about all this, did ultimately shed a memorable one. Having thus fallen from grace (indeed he had already been discovered entertaining some Papal Bulls) Wolsey determined to make a Pilgrimage to Leicester Abbey, saying to himself: 'If I had served my God as I have served my King, I would have been a Good Thing.' Having thus acknowledged that he

*NOTE – All except Anne of Cloves, whom he had on approval from Belgium and sent back on discovering that she was really not a queen at all but a 'fat mare with glanders'.

was a Bad Man, and being in due course arrived at the Abbey, Wolsey very pluckily expired after making a memorable speech to the Prior, beginning, 'Father Abbot, I come to lay my bones among you, Not to praise them . . .'

The Monasteries

One of the strongest things that Henry VIII did was about the Monasteries. It was pointed out to him that no one in the monasteries was married, as the Monks all thought it was still the Middle Ages. So Henry, who, of course, considered marrying a Good Thing, told Cromwell to pass a very strong Act saying that the Middle Ages were all over and the monasteries were all to be dissolved. This was called the Disillusion of the Monasteries.

CHAPTER 32

Edward VI and Broody Mary

EDWARD VI and Broody Mary were the two small Tudors who came in between the two big ones, Henry VIII and Elizabeth. Edward VI was only a boy and consequently was not allowed to have his reign properly, but while he was sitting on the throne everyone in the land was forced to become Protestant, so that Broody Mary would be able to put them to death afterwards for not being Roman Catholics. A good many people protested against this treatment and thus it was proved that they were Protestants, but most of the people decanted and were all right. Broody Mary's reign was, however, a Bad Thing, since England is bound to be C. of E., so all the executions were wasted.

Cramber and Fatimer

It was about this time that a memorable Dumb Crammer and one of Henry VIII's wives called Fatimer, who had survived him, got burnt alive at Oxford, while trying to light a candle in the Martyr's memorial there: it was a new candle which they had invented and which they said could never be put out.

Her heart

Shortly after this the cruel Queen died and a post-mortem examination revealed the word 'CALLOUS' engraved on her heart.

CHAPTER 33

Elizabeth

ALTHOUGH this memorable Queen was a man, she was constantly addressed by her courtiers by various affectionate female nicknames, such as Auroraborealis, Ruritania, Black Beauty (or Bête Noire), and Brown Bess. She also very graciously walked on Sir Walter Raleigh's overcoat whenever he dropped it in the mud and was, in fact, in every respect a good and romantic Queen.

Wave of Beards

One of the most romantic aspects of the Elizabethan age was the wave of beards which suddenly swept across

Wave of Beards

History and settled upon all the great men of the period. The most memorable of these beards was the cause of the outstanding event of the reign, which occurred in the following way.

The Great Armadillo

The Spaniards complained that Captain F. Drake, the memorable bowlsman, had singed the King of Spain's beard (or Spanish Mane, as it was called) one day when it was in Cadiz Harbour. Drake replied that he was in his hammock at the time and a thousand miles away. The King of Spain, however, insisted that the beard had been spoilt and sent the Great Spanish Armadillo to ravish the shores of England.

The crisis was boldly faced in England, especially by Big Bess herself, who instantly put on an enormous

Spanish Mane

quantity of clothing and rode to and fro on a white horse at Tilbury – a courageous act which was warmly applauded by the English sailors.

In this striking and romantic manner the English were once more victorious.

The Queen of Hearts

A great nuisance in this reign was the memorable Scottish queen, known as Mary Queen of Hearts on account of the large number of husbands which she obtained, e.g. Cardinale Ritzio, Boswell, and the King of France: most of these she easily blew up at Holywood.

Unfortunately for Mary, Scotland was now suddenly overrun by a wave of Synods led by Sir John Nox, the memorable Scottish Saturday Knight. Unable to believe, on account of the number of her husbands, that Mary was a single person, the Knight accused her of being a 'monstrous regiment of women', and after making this brave remark had her imprisoned in Loch Lomond. Mary, however, escaped and fled to England, where Elizabeth immediately put her in quarantine on the top of an enormous Height called Wutheringay.

As Mary had already been Queen of France and Queen of Scotland many people thought that it would be unfair if she was not made Queen of England as well. Various plots, such as the Paddington Plot, the Thread-needle Conspiracy and the Adelfi Plot, were therefore hatched to bring this about. Elizabeth, however, learning that in addition to all this Mary was good-looking and could play on the virginals, recognized that Mary was too romantic not to be executed, and accordingly had that done.

Massacre of St Bartholomew

Further evidence of Queen Elizabeth's chivalrous nature is given by her sympathy towards the French Protestants or Hugonauts (so called on account of their romantic leader Victor Hugo). These Arguenots were very much incensed at this time about St Bartholomew, a young Saint, who had been unjustly massacred for refusing to tie a white handkerchief round his arm. After the massacre the French King, Henry of Navarre, turned Roman Catholic and made his memorable con- fession – 'Paris is rather a Mess'; whereupon Queen Elizabeth very gallantly sent her favourite, Leicester, to find out whether this was true, thus rendering valuable assistance to the Hugonot cause.

Elizabeth and Essex

Memorable amongst the men with beards in Elizabeth's reign was the above-mentioned favourite, Essex (Robert Dudleigh, Earl of Leicester), whom she brought to execution by mistake in the following romantic manner. Essex was sent to Ireland to quell a rebellion which the Irish were very treacherously carrying on in a bog in Munster. Becoming fatigued with the rebellion, however, he dashed out of the bog straight into the Queen's bedroom. For this Essex was sent to the Tower, where he was shortly afterwards joined by other favourites of the Queen (such as Burleigh, Sidneigh, Watneigh, Hurlingham, etc.). Essex had a secret arrangement with Queen Elizabeth that he was to give her a ring whenever he was going to be executed, and she would reprieve him. But although, according to the arrangement, he tried to get into communication with the Queen, he was given the wrong number and was thus executed after all, along with the other favourites.

'God may forgive you,' was Brown Bess's memorable comment to the operator, 'but I never will.'

CHAPTER 34

James I: A Tidy King

JAMES I slobbered at the mouth and had favourites; he was thus a Bad King. He had, however, a very logical and tidy mind, and one of the first things he did was to have Sir Walter Raleigh executed for being left over from the previous reign. He also tried to straighten out the memorable confusion about the Picts, who, as will be remembered, were originally Irish living in Scotland, and the Scots, originally Picts living in Ireland. James tried to make things tidier by putting the Scots in Ulsters and planting them in Ireland, but the plan failed because the Picts had been lost sight of during the Dark Ages and were now nowhere to be found.

Gunpowder Plot

There were a great many plots and Parliaments in James I's reign, and one of the Parliaments was called the Addled Parliament because the plots hatched in it were all such rotten ones. One plot, however, was by far the best plot in History, and the day and month of it (though not, of course, the year) are well known to be *utterly* and even maddeningly MEMORABLE.

The Gunpowder Plot arose in the following way: the King had recently invented a new table called *Avoirduroi*, which said:

> 1 New Presbyter = 1 OLD PRIEST.
> 0 Bishop   = 0 King.

James was always repeating, 'No Bishop, No King', to himself, and one day a certain loyal citizen called Sir Guyfawkes, a very active and conscientious man, overheard him, and thought it was the slogan of James's new policy. So he decided to carry it out at once and made a very loyal plan to blow up the King and the bishops and everybody else in Parliament assembled, with gunpowder.* Although the plan failed, attempts are made every year on St Guyfawkes' Day to remind the Parliament that it would have been a *Good Thing*.

Pilgrims' Progress

It was at this time that some very pious Englishmen, known as the Early Fathers, who were being persecuted for not learning *Avoirduroi*, sailed away to America in a ship called the *Mayfly*; this is generally referred to as the Pilgrims' Progress and was one of the chief causes of America.

CHAPTER 35

Charles I and the Civil War

WITH the ascension of Charles I to the throne we come at last to the Central Period of English History (not to be confused with the Middle Ages, of course), consisting in the *utterly memorable Struggle between the Cavaliers (Wrong but Wromantic) and the Roundheads (Right and Repulsive)*.

Charles I was a Cavalier King and therefore had a small pointed beard, long flowing curls, a large, flat, flowing hat, and *gay attire*. The Roundheads, on the other hand, were clean-shaven and wore tall, conical

*Recently invented by Francis Bacon, author of Shakespeare, etc.

hats, white ties, and *sombre garments*. Under these circumstances a Civil War was inevitable.

Under these circumstances

The Roundheads, of course, were so called because Cromwell had all their heads made perfectly round, in order that they should present a uniform appearance when drawn up in line.

Besides this, if any man lost his head in action, it could be used as a cannon-ball by the artillery (which was done at the Siege of Worcester).

Competition of Right

For a long time before the Civil War, however, Charles had been quarrelling with the Roundheads about what was right. Charles explained that there was a doctrine called the Divine Right of Kings, which said that:

(a) He was King, and that was right.
(b) Kings were divine, and that was right.
(c) Kings were right, and that was right.
(d) Everything was all right.

But so determined were the Roundheads that all this was all wrong that they drew up a Petition called the Petition of Right to show in more detail which things were wrong. This Petition said:

(a) That it was wrong for anyone to be put to death more than once for the same offence.
(b) *Habeas Corpus*, which meant that it was wrong if people were put in prison except for some reason, and that people who had been mutilated by the King, such as Prynne, who had often had his ears cut off, should always be allowed to keep their bodies.
(c) That Charles's memorable methods of getting money, such as Rummage and Scroungeage, were wrong.

But the most important cause of the Civil War was

Ship Money

Charles I said that any money which was Ship Money belonged to him; but while the Roundheads declared that Ship Money could be found only in the Cinq Ports, Charles maintained that no one but the King could guess right which was Ship Money and which wasn't. This was, of course, part of his Divine Right. The climax came when a villager called Hampden (memorable for his dauntless breast) advised the King to divine again.

This so upset Charles that he went back to Westminster, and after cinquing several ports burst into the House of Commons and asked in a very royal way for some birds which he said were in there. The Parliament, who were mostly Puritans, were so shocked that they began making solemn Leagues and Countenances. Charles therefore became very angry and complaining that the birds had flown raised his standard at Nottingham and declared war against Hampden and the Roundheads.

The War

At first the King was successful owing to Prince Rupert of Hentzau, his famous cavalry leader, who was very dashing in all directions. After this, many indecisive battles were fought at such places as Newbury, Edgehill, Newbury, Chalgrove Field, Newbury, etc., in all of which the Cavaliers were rather victorious.

The Roundheads therefore made a new plan in order to win the war after all. This was called the Self-Denying Ordnance and said that everyone had to deny everything he had done up to that date, and that nobody was allowed to admit who he was: thus the war could be started again from the beginning. When the Roundheads had done this they were called the New Moral Army and were dressed up as Ironclads and put under the command of Oliver Cromwell, whose Christian name was Oliver and who was therefore affectionately known as 'Old Nick'. Cromwell was not only moral and completely round in the head but had a large (round) wart on the nose. He was consequently victorious in all the remaining battles such as Newbury, Marston Moor, Edgehill (change for Chalgrove), Naseby, Newbury, etc.

Blood and Ironclads

When Charles I had been defeated he was brought to trial by the Rump Parliament – so-called because it had been sitting for such a long time – and was found guilty of being defeated in a war against himself, which was, of course, a form of High Treason. He was therefore ordered by Cromwell to go and have his head cut off (it was, the Roundheads pointed out, the wrong shape, anyway). So romantic was Charles, however, that this made little difference to him and it is very memorable that he walked and talked Half an hour after his Head was cut off.

Very memorable

On seeing this, Cromwell was so angry that he picked up the mace (the new and terrible Instrument of Government which he had invented) and, pointing it at the Head, shouted: 'Take away that Marble,' and announced that his policy in future would be just Blood and Ironclads. In order to carry out this policy he divided the country into twelve districts and set a Serjeant-Major over each of them.

Rule of the Serjeant-Majors

Nothing sickened the people of the rule of the Serjeant-Majors so much as their cruel habit of examining little boys *viva-voce*. For this purpose the unfortunate children were dressed in their most uncomfortable satins and placed on a stool. The Serjeant-Major would then ask such difficult questions as 'How's your Father?' or 'Animal, Vegetable, or Mineral?' and those

who could not answer were given a cruel medicine called Pride's Purge. All this was called the Crommonwealth and was right but repulsive.

The Crowning Mercy

The Roundheads at length decided to offer Cromwell the Crown. Cromwell, however, was unwilling and declared it was a Crowning Mercy when he found that it would not fit, having been designed for a Cavalier King.

Soon after, Cromwell died of a surfeit of Pride, Purges, Warts, and other Baubles.

CHAPTER 36

Charles II: A Merry Monarch

CHARLES II was always very merry and was therefore not so much a king as a Monarch. During the civil war he had rendered valuable assistance to his father's side by hiding in all the oak-trees he could find. He was thus very romantic and popular and was able after the death of Cromwell to descend to the throne.

Though now no longer arboreal, Charles remained

A Bad Man

very much interested in natural beauty and kept a great number of pets at his court, including his famous *King*

77

Charles's Spaniards, the most memorable of whom was Catherine of Braganza; but, although married to Catherine, Charles was even fonder of an orange girl called Elinor Gwyn. He was thus a Bad Man.

The Reformation

Charles II was famous for his wit and his inventions. Among the latter was an unbridled and merry way of behaving and writing plays, called the Reformation. This was a Good Thing in the end as it was one of the earliest causes of Queen Victoria's determination to be good.

Examples of Charles's Wit

Most of Charles's witty remarks were of an *unbridled nature* and are therefore (fortunately) *not memorable*.

He instituted, however, a number of witty Acts of Parliament. Amongst these were:

(*a*) The *Act of Indemnity and Oblivion*, which said that everyone had to pay an indemnity to the King and then forget that he had paid it.

(*b*) The *Act of Uniformity*, which said that everyone had to be the same as everyone else.

(*c*) The *Five Mile Act*, which said that no schoolmasters or clergymen were to go within five miles of each other. (This was, obviously, a Good Thing.)

(*d*) The *Corporation Act*, which said that everyone had to be as fat as possible (except Nell Glyn).

After each of these Charles became merrier still and though some of them, particularly the Corporation Act, were considered rather unfair, he made up by passing a new Habeas Corpus Act which said that *all* the people might keep their bodies, and thus everyone was contented. Later, Charles became even merrier and made a *Declaration of Indulgence* saying that people could do anything they liked and a *Test Act* was passed soon after to see if they had done it (and, if so, what).

Admiral De Trop in the Channel (*Reuter*)

It was at this period that the Navigation Acts were first made by the English. These Acts pointed out to the other countries that no foreign ships knew how to navigate the seas, and that their only chance was to steer for English ports. Although this was really part of the Rule Britannia (see Chap. 2, Freedom of the Seas), it caused some wars against the Dutch who were treacherously attempting to be top nation on the sea at that time. For a short while the Dutch ships were successful under their memorable Admiral, Van Broom, who is famous for blowing his own Trompet up the Medway until the sound was heard in the streets of London. The war, however, soon came to an end, since the Dutch are quite small and can never be top nation really.

Quaker Oates

A great deal of excitement was caused in this reign by Titus Oates, the memorable Quaker, who said that a Roman Catholic plot had been made with the objects

(*a*) of murdering the King, (*b*) of blowing up the people, (*c*) of restoring the Roman Catholic religion instead.

79

These would probably have been a Bad Thing, if they had been achieved, and the King was so enraged that he immediately introduced a *Disabling Act* which said that everyone except the heir to the throne was to be disabled. Later when he had relented, he had another *Habeas Corpus Act* passed, saying that the disabled people might keep their bodies.

Two Good Things

During Charles II's reign the Great Plague happened in London. This was caused by some rats which had left a sinking ship on its way from China, and was very fortunate for the Londoners, since there were too many people in London at the time, so that they were always in bad health.

In the following year, therefore, London was set on fire in case anyone should have been left over from the Plague, and St Paul's Cathedral was built instead. This was also a Good Thing and was the cause of Sir Christopher Wren, the memorable architect.

Pepys

Among the famous characters of the period were Samuel Pepys, who is memorable for keeping a Dairy and going to bed a great deal, and his wife Evelyn, who kept another memorable Dairy, but did not go to bed in in it.

CHAPTER 37

James II: A Maddening King

ALTHOUGH a Good Man, James II was a Bad King and behaved in such an irritating and arbitrary way that by the end of his reign the people had all gone mad.

Judge Jeffreys

One of the first things that happened was a rebellion by Monmouth, an indiscriminate son of Charles II who, landing incorrectly in Somerset, was easily defeated at

Bloody Asides

Newbury, Sedgehill, Marston Moor, Newbury, etc. (see Civil War). The Rebels were ferociously dealt with by the memorable Judge Jeffreys who was sent out by

James as a Justice in Ire in the West, where he made some furious remarks about the prisoners, known as 'The Bloody Asides'.

Madnesses of James II

James II further enraged his subjects by

(*a*) attempting to repeal the Habeas Corpus Act, saying that nobody might have a body after all, and

(*b*) claiming the Dispensing Power which was a threat to revive Pride's Purge and do the dispensing of it himself;

(*c*) suspending (probably a modified form of hanging) the Vice-Chancellor at Cambridge, who was apparently mad too, for refusing to have a Benedictine.

England's Answer

The final and irreparable madness of the people was brought on by James's action in bringing to trial Seven Bishops (Bancroft, Sancroft, and Sacheveral others) for refusing to read Charles II's Declaration of Indulgence (which they thought would be dangerous under the circumstances), and when in addition it became known that James had confined his infant son and heir in a warming-pan the people lost control of themselves altogether and, lighting an enormous number of candles, declared that *the answer was an Orange*. James was thus compelled to abdicate.

CHAPTER 38

Williamanmary: England Ruled by an Orange

WILLIAMANMARY for some reason was known as The Orange in their own country of Holland, and were popular as King of England because the people naturally believed it was descended from Nell Glyn. It

The Answer

was on the whole a good King and one of their first Acts was the Toleration Act, which said they would tolerate anything, though afterwards it went back on this and decided that they could not tolerate the Scots.

A Darien Scheme

The Scots were now in a skirling uproar because James II was the last of the Scottish Kings and England was under the rule of the Dutch Orange; it was therefore decided to put them in charge of a very fat man called Cortez and transport them to a Peak in Darien, where it was hoped they would be more silent.

The Scots, however, continued to squirl and hoot at the Orange, and a rebellion was raised by the memorable Viscount Slaughterhouse (the Bonnie Dundee) and his Gallivanting Army. Finally Slaughterhouse was defeated at the Pass of Ghilliekrankie and the Scots were all massacred at Glascoe, near Edinburgh (in Scotland, where the Scots were living at that time); after which they were forbidden to curl or hoot or even to wear the Kilt. (This was a Good Thing, as the Kilt was one of the causes of their being so uproarious and Scotch.)

Blood-Orangemen

Meanwhile the Orange increased its popularity and showed themselves to be a very strong King by its ingenious answer to the Irish Question; this consisted in the Battle of the Boyne and a very strong treaty which followed it, stating

(*a*) that all the Irish Roman Catholics who liked could be transported to France,

(*b*) that all the rest who liked could be put to the sword,

(*c*) that Northern Ireland should be planted with Blood-Orangemen.

These Blood-Orangemen are still there; they are, of course, all descendants of Nell Glyn and are extremely fierce and industrial and so loyal that they are always ready to start a loyal rebellion to the Glory of God and the Orange. All of which shows that the Orange was a Good Thing, as well as being a good King.

After the Treaty the Irish who remained were made to go and live in a bog and think of a New Question.

The Bank of England

It was Williamanmary who first discovered the National Debt and had the memorable idea of building the Bank of England to put it in. The National Debt is a very Good Thing and it would be dangerous to pay it off, for fear of Political Economy.

Finally the Orange was killed by a mole while out riding and was succeeded by the memorable dead queen, Anne.

TEST PAPER IV

Up to the End of the Stuarts

1. Stigmatize cursorily (*a*) Queen Mary, (*b*) Judge Jeffreys's asides. (Speak out.)
2. Outline joyfully (1) Henry VIII, (2) Stout Cortez.
3. Who had what written on whose what?
4A. What convinces you that Henry VIII had VIII wives? Was it worth it?
4B. Conjugate briefly Ritzio and Mary Queen of Scots.
5. In what ways was Queen Elizabeth a Bad Man but a Good Queen?
6. 'To the exercise of Despotic Monarchy the Crown is more essential than the Throne.' (Refute with special reference to anything you know.)
7A. Which do you consider was the stronger swimmer, (*a*) The Spanish Armadillo, (*b*) The Great Seal?
7B. Who was in whose what, and how many miles awhat?

7C. Cap'n, art thou sleeping there below ?*

8. Deplore the failure of the Gunpowder Plot, stating the day and month (but not, of course, the year) usually assigned to it.

9. Examine the state of mind of
   (1) Charles I, half an hour after his head was cut off
   (2) Charles II, half a moment after first sighting Nell Gwyn.

10. Why on earth was William of Orange ? (Seriously, though.)

11. How can you be so numb and vague about Arabella Stuart ?

12. Estimate the medical prowess of the period with clinical reference to (*a*) Pride's Purge, (*b*) The Diet of Worms, (*c*) The Topic of Capricorns.

*N.B. – Do not attempt to answer this question.

CHAPTER 39

Anne: A Dead Queen

QUEEN ANNE was considered rather a remarkable woman and hence was usually referred to as Great Anna, or Annus Mirabilis. Besides being dead she was extremely kind-hearted and had a very soothing Act passed called the *Occasional Conformity Act* which said that people only had to conform with it occasionally: this pleasant trait in her character was called Queen Anne's Bounty. (The Occasional Conformity Act was the only Act of its kind in History, until the Speed limit was invented.)

The Queen had many favourites (all women), the

most memorable of whom were Sarah Jenkins and Mrs Smashems, who were the first Wig and the first Tory. Sarah Jenkins was really the wife of the Duke of Marlborough, the famous General, inventor of the Ramillies Whig, of which Sarah wore the first example.

Succession of Wars

All through the eighteenth century there was a Succession of Wars, and in Queen Anne's reign these were called the Spanish Succession (or Austrian Succession) because of The Infanta (or The Mariatheresa); they were fought mainly on account of the French King L/XIV (le grand Monomarque) saying there were *no more Pyrenese*, thus infuriating the Infanta who was one herself.

Probably the Wars could never have been fought properly but for the genius of Marlborough, who could always remember which side the Bavarians and the Elector Pantomime of the Rhine were supposed to be on: this unique talent enabled him to defeat his enemies in fierce battles long before they could discover which side he himself was on. Marlborough, however, was a miser in politics and made everyone pay to go into his party; he was therefore despised as a *turnstyle*.

In this reign also occurred the memorable Port Wine Treaty with Portugal, directed against Decanters (as the Non-Conformists were now called), as well as a very clever Act called the Schism Act which said that everybody's religion was to be quite different from everybody else's. Meanwhile the Whigs being the first to realize that the Queen had been dead all the time chose George I as King.

CHAPTER 40

The XV and the XLV

ALTHOUGH the Whigs said that George I was King, many of the Tories thought that the Old Pretender was. The Old Pretender did not raise the standard of rebellion much and is only famous for being late for his own Rebellion, which had been easily put down long before he landed with his memorable XV in Scotland. His standard was of blue silk with the motto '*Nemo me impune lacessit*', but when it was raised the top fell off.

The Young Pretender, whose followers were called the XLV, was quite different, his standard being of red silk with the motto '*Tandem Triumphans*', and the top didn't fall off. At Preston Pans the English commander was the first to run away and bring the news of his own defeat, which was thus immediately believed. The hero of these adventures was the memorable Bonnie Prince Charlie (the Young Chandelier), who after being bloodily defeated by a Butcher at Flodden in Cumberland, was helped to escape by his many Scottish lovers, such as Flora MacNightingale (the fair maid of Perth), Amy Robsart, Lorna Doone, Annie Laurie, the Widow with Thumbs, etc.

The Southsea Bubble

About this time nearly everybody in London stupidly got involved in an enormous bubble that appeared at Southsea. Some were persuaded that it would be a

Good Thing if all the money in the country, including the National Debt, were sunk in it; others got into it merely with the object of speculating how soon it would be before it burst. Among these was a very clever man called Walpole who got out of the bubble in time, thus bursting it and becoming the first Prime Minister. Walpole was a Good Prime Minister: the Southsea bubble was thus a Good Thing.

'Let Sleeping Dogs Lie' (*Walpole*)

Walpole ought never to be confused with Walpole, who was quite different; it was Walpole who lived in a house with the unusual name of Strawberry Jam and spent his time writing letters to famous men (such as the Prime Minister, Walpole, etc.). Walpole is memorable for inventing the new policy of letting dogs go to sleep.

Policy

This was a Good Thing really, but it so enraged the people (who thought that a dog's life should be more uncomfortable) that they rang all the bells in London. At first Walpole merely muttered his policy, but eventually he was compelled to rouse himself and become actively memorable by remarking: 'They are ringing the bells now; I shall be wringing their necks soon.'

CHAPTER 41

Rules of Wars in the Eighteenth Century

ALTHOUGH the Succession of Wars went on nearly the whole time in the eighteenth century, the countries kept on making a treaty called the Treaty of Paris (or Utrecht).

This Treaty was a Good Thing and laid down the Rules for fighting the wars; these were:

(1) that there should be a mutual restitution of conquests except that England should keep Gibraltar, Malta, Minorca, Canada, India, etc.;

(2) that France should hand over to England the West Indian islands of San Flamingo, Tapioca, Sago, Dago, Bezique and Contango, while the Dutch were always to have Lumbago and the Laxative Islands;

(3) that everyone, however Infantile or even insane, should renounce all claim to the Spanish throne;

(4) that the King (or Queen) of France should admit that the King (or Queen) of England was King (or Queen) of England and should not harbour the Young Pretender, but that *the fortifications of Dunkirk should be disgruntled and raised to the ground.*

Thus, as soon as the fortifications of Dunkirk had been gruntled again, or the Young Pretender was found in a harbour in France, or it was discovered that the Dutch had not got Lumbago, etc., the countries knew that it was time for the treaty to be signed again, so that the War could continue in an orderly manner.

CHAPTER 42

George III: An Obstinate King

GEORGE III was a Bad King. He was, however, to a great extent insane and a Good Man and his ministers were always called Pitt. The Pitts, like Pretenders, generally came in waves of about two, an elder Pitt and a younger Pitt.

Britain Muffles Through

The elder Pitt (Clapham) at this time had the rather strategic idea of conquering Canada on the banks of the Elbe; learning, however, that it was not there, he told the famous poetic general, Wolfe, to conquer Quebec instead. At first Wolfe complained that he would rather write Gray's Elegy, but on being told that it had been written already (by Gray) he agreed to take Quebec.

Quebec was very difficult to approach; Wolfe therefore rowed up the St Laurence with muffled drums and ordered his Highland troops to skirl up the perpendicular Heights of Abraham with muffled boots, hoots, etc., thus taking the French by surprise.

At this engagement the French had a very peculiar general with the unusual French name of Keep-calm.

On receiving a muffled report to the effect that Wolfe's men had captured Quebec, one of his aides-de-

Wave of Pitts

calm called out: 'See! They fly!' 'Who fly?' asked the General, and, on being assured that it was his own men who were flying, 'Thank God!' said Keep-calm, with a sigh of satisfaction: 'Now, I can fly in peace!'

Britain muffles through

CHAPTER 43

India

IT was in the eighteenth century that Indian History started. Indian History is a great number of wars in which the English fought victoriously against the Waratah Confederacy and various kinds of potentates called Sahibs, Wallahs, Jahs, Rajahs, Hurrahjahs, Mahurrahjahs, Jhams, and Jhelhies. Most memorable amongst these were the terrible Napoo Sahib, the Maharatta of Pshaw, the Chandra Gaff, and the Taj Mahal.

Cressey and the Black Whole

Many of these victories were due to an Englishman named Robert Clive, a typist in the East India Coy Ltd, who, after failing to commit suicide three times, made the famous raid on Arcos in conjunction with Jicks Pasha, and held it against all comers.

Clive then marched to Calcutta and with a Mir Jafar (or handful) of men defeated all the Indians in the utterly memorable battle of Cressey.

This battle was Clive's revenge on the Black Whole of Calcutta and especially on that destructive All-Black Waratah, the Napoo Sahib.

The Doldrums of Oudh

Second in importance only to Clive was Laurence Hastings, well known for his rapacity towards the natives. Besides his treatment of Lo (a poor Indian with an untutored mind) recorded by the poet Poep, he very harshly extracted money from the Doldrums of Oudh, two old women without any teeth. For this he was impaled before the House of Commons, and after being cross-examined by Burke and Hare for seven and a half years, was finally acquitted and became Viscount Senlac of Oudh.

CHAPTER 44

The Boston Tea-Party

ONE day when George III was insane he heard that the Americans never had afternoon tea. This made him very obstinate and he invited them all to a compulsory tea-party at Boston; the Americans, however, started by pouring the tea into Boston Harbour and went on pouring things into Boston Harbour until they were quite Independent, thus causing the United States. These were also partly caused by Dick Washington who defeated the English at Bunker's Hill ('with his little mashie', as he told his father afterwards).

The War with the Americans is memorable as being the only war in which the English were ever defeated, and it was unfair because the Americans had *the Allies* on their side. In some ways the war was really a draw, since England remained top nation and had the Allies afterwards, while the Americans, in memory of George III's madness, still refuse to drink tea and go on pouring anything the English send them to drink into Boston Harbour.

After this the Americans made Wittington President and gave up speaking English and became U.S.A. and Columbia and 100%, etc. This was a Good Thing in the end, as it was a cause of the British Empire, but it prevented America from having any more History.

100%, etc.

CHAPTER 45

The French Revolution

SOON after America had ceased to be memorable, the French Revolution broke out (in France). This, like all other Revolutions, was chiefly due to Liberty, Fraternity, Equality, etc., but also to the writings of Madame Tousseau, the French King's mistress, who believed in everyone returning to a state of nature and was therefore known as *la belle sauvage*.

The French Revolution is very interesting and

romantic; quite near the beginning of it Dante and Robespear, the revolutionary leaders (or *Jacobites* as they were called), met in the beautiful and historic Chamber of Horrors at Versailles and decided to massacre everyone in September. This was called the *Glorious First of June* and was done in accordance with a new *National Convention*. Memorable amongst those who were massacred were Robespear himself, who was executed in his own gelatine, and Marat, who was murdered in his bath by Madame Tousseau.

CHAPTER 46

Napoleon

THE English were disgusted by this new French Convention and so decided to go in for The War again, thus causing Nelson and the Duke of Wellington. The War was now called the Napoleonic War, after Napoleon, a Corsican, whose real name was Bonuapart, and who had cleverly made himself First Consort by means of a *whiff of grape-nuts*. (This is called the Napoleonic Legend.)

The French Revolution caused great loss of life, liberty, fraternity, etc., and was, of course, a Good Thing, since the French were rather degenerate at the time; but Napoleon now invented a new Convention that the French should massacre all the other nations and become top nation, and this, though quite generate, was a Bad Thing.

CHAPTER 47

Nelson

NAPOLEON ought never to be confused with Nelson, in spite of their hats being so alike; they can most easily be distinguished from one another by the fact that Nelson always stood with his arm *like this*, while Napoleon always stood with his arms *like that*.

Nelson was one of England's most naval officers, and despised weak commands. At one battle when he was told that his Admiral-in-Chief had ordered him to cease fire, he put the telephone under his blind arm and exclaimed in disgust: 'Kiss me, Hardy!'

By this and other intrepid manoeuvres the French were utterly driven from the seas.

Pitt and Fox

Meanwhile at home the War was being helped on a good deal by the famous remarks of the politicians, such as Pitt and Fox. On one occasion Fox said in the House of Commons that the French Revolution was a Good Thing; whereupon the younger Pitt (Balham) rose slowly to his feet and, pointing at Fox, exclaimed: 'Roll up that chap: he will not be wanted these ten years.' Having thus made his most memorable saying, Pitt was carried out of the House and died almost immediately of a surfeit of austerlitz. The plans of Napoleon were thus gradually thwarted.

CHAPTER 48

Wellington

But the most important of the great men who at this time kept Britain top nation was an Irishman called John Wesley, who afterwards became the Duke of Wellington (and thus English). When he was still Wolseley, Wellington made a great name for himself at Plassaye, in India, where he

'Fought with his fiery few and one',

remarking afterwards, 'It was the bloodiest battle for numbers I ever knew.' It was, however, against Napoleon and his famous Marshals (such as Marshals

To march on their Stomachs

Ney, Soult, Davos, Mürren, Soult, Blériot, Snelgrove, Ney, etc.) that Wellington became most memorable. Napoleon's armies always used to march on their stomachs, shouting: 'Vive l'Intérieur!' and so moved about very slowly (*ventre-à-terre*, as the French say), thus enabling Wellington to catch them up and defeat them. When Napoleon made his troops march all the way to Moscow on their stomachs they got frozen to death one by one, and even Napoleon himself admitted afterwards that it was rather a Bad Thing.

Gorilla War in Spain

The second part of the Napoleonic War was fought in Spain and Portugal and was called the Gorilla War on account of the primitive Spanish method of fighting.

Gorilla Warfare

Wellington became so impatient with the slow movements of the French troops that he occupied himself drawing imaginary lines all over Portugal and thus marking off the fighting zone; he made a rule that defeats beyond these lines did not count, while any French army that came his side of them was out of bounds. Having thus insured himself against disaster, Wellington won startling victories at Devalera, Albumina, Salamanda, etc.

After losing this war Napoleon was sent away by the French, since he had not succeeded in making them top nation; but he soon escaped and returned just in time to fight on the French side at the battle of Waterloo. This utterly memorable battle was fought at the end of a dance, on the Playing Fields of Eton, and resulted in the English definitely becoming top nation. It was thus a very Good Thing. During the engagement the French came on in their usual creeping and crawling method and were defeated by Wellington's memorable order, 'Up Jenkins and Smashems'.

This time Napoleon was sent right away for ever by everybody, and stood on the deck of a ship in white breeches with his arms *like that*.

CHAPTER 49

The Industrial Revelation

DURING these Wars many very remarkable discoveries and inventions were made. Most memorable among these was the discovery (made by all the rich men in England at once) that women and children could work for twenty-five hours a day in factories without many of them dying or becoming excessively deformed. This was known as the Industrial Revelation and completely changed the faces of the North of England.

The Industrial Revelation would never have occurred but for the wave of great mechanical Inventors, e.g. Arkwright, who invented the Spinning Jenny, or unmarried textile working girl; subsequently, however, this kind of work was done by mules, the discovery of a man called Crompton. Other benefactors were Sir Isaak Watts who invented steam-kettles, Sir Robert Boyle

Mr Arkwright's Invention

who had them legalized,* and finally Robert Louis Stevenson, who put wheels on to them, thereby inventing Railway trains, steam-rollers, and other tractarian engines.

Factory Acts

The new situation created by the Industrial Revelation was boldly met by the statesmen of the day with a wave of Acts, such as Tory Acts, Factory Acts, Satisfactory Acts and Unsatisfactory Acts. The most soothing of

*Boyle's Law: 'Watts pots never boyle.'

these enacted that children under five years of age who worked all day in factories should have meals (at night). This was a Good Thing, as it enabled them to work much faster.

Enclosures

At the same time there was an Agricultural Revelation which was caused by the invention of turnips and the discovery that Trespassers would be Prosecuted. This was a Good Thing too, because previously the Land had all been rather common, and it was called the Enclosure movement and was the origin of Keeping off the Grass. The movement culminated in the vast Royal Enclosure at Ascot which nobody is allowed on except His Majesty the King (and friend).

The Combinations Law

All this gave rise to considerable discontent, but it was not until the memorable Combinations Law was passed that the people were roused to fury. This unjust law

Combinations Law

said that Combinations (or Union suits) were legal, or (in some cases) illegal, both for employers and employees, and resulted in the

Blankester Massacre

Gradually the people had become so discontented with the Combinations Law that they had begun wearing Blankets, especially in the North of England; this was of course, sedition, and resulted in a battle near Manchester, in which all the people in blankets were accidentally massacred.

The Government then very cleverly passed the famous Six Acts, all of which said that it was quite all right for people in blankets to be massacred. Since which the people in the North have ceased to be seditious, and even wear bowler hats for lunch, bathing, etc.

Munroe Doctrine

Meanwhile in foreign affairs, Canning, the memorable foreign minister, started a new anti-English or Liberal policy by saying that he had 'called the New World into existence to upset the Balance of the Old'. This was known as the Munroe Doctrine and proves that it is wrong for anyone to have wars in North or South America (except the United States Marines).

CHAPTER 50

George IV: A Gentleman King

DURING these disturbances George III had died and had been succeeded by his son, George IV, who was the Prince Regent and an Inventor and very Bad. George IV's most memorable invention was Gentlemen and he was the First Gentleman in Europe:

Examples of George IV's Badness and Gentlemanliness

1. He was very fat.
2. He was a friend of Beau Brocade, the memorable Dandy Dinmont or man-about-town of those days.
3. He was a member of White's and many other notorious Knight clubs.
4. He was hostile to his wife and attempted to give her pains by means of an Act of Parliament.

Death of George IV

Besides gentlemen, George IV had invented Regent Street, the Regent Canal, etc., before he came to the throne, and afterwards he invented the Brighton Marine Aquarium. He was thus a Bad Thing. Finally he died of a surfeit of Aquaria, Pavilia, Gentlemen, etc., probably at Brighton.

CHAPTER 51

William IV: A Sailor King

THE marine tendency of George IV was inherited by his brother William IV, who was known as the Sailor King on account of his readiness to create any number of piers at moments of political crisis. Apart from this, however, William IV would not have succeeded in being memorable at all except for his awkward and un-called-for irruption into the Georgian succession.

Rotten Burrows

During this reign the Great Reform Bill was passed on account of the Rotten Burrows: this was because the Old Landlords said that new places like Manchester were rotten burrows and shouldn't have votes. A great deal of confusion was caused by these rotten burrows which were undermining the Constitution, but eventually Lord Grey invented the Great Reform Bill which laid down clearly who had votes and who hadn't.

Reform Bill

This Bill had two important clauses, which said:

(1) that some of the Burrows were rotten and that the people who lived in them should not be allowed either to stand or to have seats.
(2) that 'householders leaseholders and copyholders who

had £10 in the towns or freeholders who paid 40s. in the country for 10 years or leaseholders (in the country) and copyholders for 21 years in the towns (paying a rent of £50) should in some cases (in the towns) have a vote (for 1 year) but in others for 41 years (in the country) paying a leasehold or copyhold of £10 should not.'

When this unforgettable Law was made known there was great rejoicing and bonfires were lit all over the country.

Later Reform Bills

Later in the century, other Reform Bills were passed, such as Gladstone's Reform Bill which added house-holders (in the country) for one year to freeholders and kettleholders worth £10 a year, and gave a vote to any-one who lived in lodgings (for 21 years) or spent £10 in the Post Office. And there was also Disraeli's Reform Bill, which gave the vote to any lodger who paid £10 and lodged in the same lodgings for one year. This, however, was naturally thought very rash and was quite rightly characterized by the penetrating Lord Salisbury, in a brilliant phrase, as 'A Sleep in the Dark'. The Reform Bills were a Good Thing except for a few Old Landlords who were deprived of their seats. Nowadays Flappers are allowed to vote and men have to put up with this even if they live in the same lodgings all their lives. This is a Bad Thing and is called Manhold Suffrage.

CHAPTER 52

Queen Victoria: A Good Queen

ON the death of William IV, Queen Victoria, though asleep at the time and thus in her nightdress, showed great devotion to duty by immediately ascending the throne. In this bold act she was assisted by Lord Melbourne and the Archbishop of Canterbury, who were both properly dressed.

Good . . . *but*
not amused

Finding herself on the throne, Queen Victoria immediately announced her intention of being Good and plural *but not amused*. This challenge was joyfully accepted by her subjects, and throughout her protracted reign *loyal and indefatigable attempts to amuse her* were made by Her Majesty's eminently Victorian ministers and generals.

Attempts to Amuse Queen Victoria

One of the first of these attempts was Lord Melbourne's

memorable political rule that it did not matter what the Cabinet said so long as they all answered at once. This he called the Collective Responsibility of the Cabinet; the Queen, however, was not amused.

Next, Mr Rowland Hill invented penny stamps. The Queen, however, without hesitation Knighted him.

To abandon all thoughts of levity –

The loyal task therefore devolved on a more active group of men called the Chartists who nearly succeeded by drawing an enormous Chart showing the position of affairs and signing it with imaginary names. This resulted in a succession of riots amongst the imaginary people, and necessitated the passing of the memorable Poor Law which laid down that everybody in the country was poor (except the rich).

These endeavours having failed, the Queen was allowed to abandon for the time being all thoughts of levity and to marry her beautiful cousin (the memorable Prince Consaught), a Good German whom she had met during the great International Expedition to Hyde Park.

About this time the famous Tory statesman, Sir Robert Repeel, noticed that the Irish had had nothing to eat for some years owing to the fact that the potatoes, which it was their Duty to eat, had all gone bad.

The Tory Government were for long divided between two policies, one section insisting that the Irish ought to eat the potatoes, the other insisting that they need not.

Sir Robert, however, boldly passed his famous Corn Laws which abolished the Duty and permitted the Irish to eat bread, thus dissociating himself from the Tories who doggedly maintained that the Irish had only two alternatives: (*a*) to eat the potatoes, and (*b*) not to. Sir Robert, having thus destroyed his own Party, bethought himself of The Queen and invented Policemen. Her Majesty, however, . . .

CHAPTER 53

Crimean War

NOT very long after this the memorable Crimean War broke out against the Russians. This war was exceptionally inevitable and was caused by a number of causes.

Causes of the Crimean War

(*a*) The English had not yet fought against the Russians.
(*b*) The *Sick Man of Europe* (cured later by Florence Nightingown).

(c) Russia was too big and was pointing in the direction of India.

(d) The *Holy Places*. *The French* thought that the *Holy Places* ought to be guarded (probably against the *Americans*) by *Latin Monks*, while *the Turks*, who owned the Places, thought that they ought to be guarded by *Greek Monks*. *England* therefore quite rightly declared war on *Russia*, who immediately occupied *Roumania*.

The war was consequently fought in *the Crimea* (near *Persia*) in the following romantic manner:

1. *The Battle of Inkerman* – so called because the soldiers on both sides fought in the dark as well as the Generals: the English were, naturally, victorious.

2. *The Siege of Sir Pastobol* (the memorable Russian General) who was quite besieged, and the English were very victorious.

3. *The Battle of Balaclava*, famous for the Charge of the Fire Brigade by Lord Tennyson and 599 other gallant men who, armed with Cardigans and Balaclava helmets,

Suffered terribly from their Cardigans and
Balaclava helmets

advanced for a league and a half (4½ miles) and back (9 miles), with the object of proving that someone had thundered the wrong order. (In which they were completely successful.)

4. *Flora MacNightshade*. The troops in the Crimea suffered terribly from their Cardigans and Balaclava helmets and from a new kind of overcoat invented by Lord Raglan, the Commander-in-Chief. They were also only allowed to wear boots on their left feet until the memorable intervention of Flora MacNightlight (the Lady with the Deadly Lampshade), who gave them boots for their right feet and other comforts, and cured them of their sufferings every night with doses of deadly lampshade.

CHAPTER 54

The Indian Mutiny

THIS was also inevitable on account of:

(a) *The Natives*. These believed that the English were going to make them bite their greasy cartileges (Chuputti). This they treacherously believed to be contrary to their religion and therefore a Bad Thing.

(b) *The Anglo-Indians*. The natives were unable to realize that these were a Good Thing.

Consequently an outbreak of very serious Meeruts occurred at Cawnpore and elsewhere and a descendant of the Great Mohawk was set up as Emperor at Dulwich (the old capital of India). Most terrible among the Indian leaders was a native Pundit called the Banana Sahib who by means of his treacherous disguise lured famished British regiments to destruction.

The Mutiny, however, was a Good Thing as it was the cause of Lucknow being relieved by Generals Havelock, Ellis, etc., and Lord Roberts got the V.C. and stayed on for forty-one years.

The Results of the Mutiny were:

(a) The Sepoy (or Governor-General) of India was brought under the control of the Crown.

(b) The Queen was declared to be the Great Mohawk of India.

CHAPTER 55

'Pal'

MEANWHILE, at home, fresh attempts to galvanize the Queen resulted in the promotion of Lord Palmerston ('Pal') to the Premiership – a rather matey minister who always wore green gloves and sucked a straw and altered the Despatches after the Queen had signed them, so that they became surprises for her. It was not, however, until he conceived and carried through his heartless *Conspiracy to Murder Bill* that the Good (but now Horrified) Queen dismissed him. After which 'Pal' spent his time taking special trains in all directions and galloping to Harrow on a cream-coloured pony, thus endearing himself to the People and becoming an object of terror and admiration to all foreign governments.

CHAPTER 56

Fresh Attempts to Amuse the Queen. Wave of Justifiable Wars

OWING to the inability of the Queen's ministers to amuse the Crown, superhuman attempts were now made by her Majesty's generals at home and abroad to provide military diversions. These took the form of a wave of Justifiable Wars, including:

1. *War with China.* Fought on moral grounds, because the Chinese government were disposed to impede the importation of Empire Opium into China. The British thus became indispensable to the Chinese and, after several bloody engagements, Hong Kong, the best port of China, was ceded to the British Throne.

2. *War with Afghanistan.* Owing to the size, direction, etc., of Russia, it was imperative that the King of Afghanistan, whose name was Just Mohammed, should sit on his throne in a friendly attitude. The King, however, (Just) declined to do this and the British Army was cut to pieces in the Pippa Passes to such an extent that Dr Brydle rode half alive (or, according to some historians, half dead) into Jallallaballad. After this, however, several bloody battles were fought, and the Kings of Afghanistan were compelled to sit in a more friendly attitude.

3. *Sheikh War.* Cause: Death of Ranji Tsinji (a huge Sheikh). The Sheikhs were very tall men on the frontier of India who obscured the Imperial outlook. A bloody strife ensued. Sir Hew Golf annihilated the Sheikhs, subsequently compelling them to present the Queen with a huge pencil called the Koh-in-Oor. The Sheikhs were

thus reduced in every way and were afterwards on our side and a Good Thing.

4. *2nd Burmese War*. Cause: there had only been one Burmese war. Burmese cut to pieces. Burma ceded to the Crown. Peace with Burma.

5. *War against Abyssinia*. Object: to release the Europeans in Abyssinia, all of whom had been incarcerated by the King, Theodore, who was a Christian and would not see their point of view. The war was divided into two parts (1) Sir Robert Rapier demands release of prisoners. Prisoners released. (2) War declared against Abyssinia. King Theodore blown up with Magnesia, the capital of Abyssinia. Theodore commits suicide. Sir Robert becomes Lord Rapier of Magnesia. Peace with Abyssinia.

6. *War against A Shantee*. Coffee, King of a Shantee, worsted and burnt by Sir Garment Wolsee, who becomes Viscount Coffee. Peace with the Shantee.

7. *War against Zulus*. Cause: the Zulus. Zulus exterminated. Peace with Zulus.

All these attempts having failed, news was brought to the Queen that the Fiji Islands were annexed to the British 'by the desire of the inhabitants'. At this point, according to some (seditious) historians, Her Majesty's lip was observed to tremble.

Spheres of Interference. Egypt

It was during these wars that Spheres of Interference were discovered: these were necessary in all Countries inhabited by their own natives.

The first of the Spheres was Egypt which now became memorable for the first time since Potiphar, the well-known Egyptian Pharaoh.

Egypt was put under the Duel Control of England and France and was thus declared bankrupt; Alibaba, the Mowhgli, and other Pasha-Beziques were therefore immediately exterminated by Sir Garment Wolsey and subsequently by Kitchener of Kartoon at the terrible French battle of Homme de Man. This was because of Chinese Gordon (leader of the famous Gordon Riots* in Pekin) and was called the Pagoda Incident and is remarkable as being the only (memorable) *Incident* in History.

CHAPTER 57

Disraeli and Gladstone

NOT very much is known about these two extremely memorable ministers, except that (*a*) *Disraeli* 'brought back Peace with Honour' after the famous Balkan Treaty of Berlin, which said:

1. that Bosnia should be ceded to Herzegovina;
2. that Herzegovina should be ceded to Bosnia (this is called the Eastern Question);
3. that Bulgaria should be divided into two parts (later, Bulgaria was re-divided into one part by Mr Gladstone);
4. that anyone found in Armenia should be gradually divided into twelve parts. (Mr Gladstone subsequently criticized the effect of this clause.)

Disraeli also very generously purchased the Panama Canal from the Khalif and presented it to Queen

*Due to the justifiable looting of Pekin by the Allies.

Victoria with a huge bunch of primroses (his favourite flower), thus becoming Lord Beaconsfield and a romantic minister. The Queen, however, remained obdurately plural and not amused, even when Disraeli romantically called her a Faery Queen.

(b) Gladstone, on the other hand, endeavoured (quite unsuccessfully) to please Her Majesty by chewing a milk pudding seventy-nine times every day, and by his memorable inventions; amongst the latter were an exceptionally uncomfortable collar which he inhabited for sixty-two years on the floor of the House of Commons, and an extremely simple kind of bag which he designed to enable the Turks to be driven out of Europe *Bag and Baggage*. Gladstone also invented the Education Rate by which it was possible to calculate how soon anybody could be educated, and spent his declining years trying to guess the answer to the Irish Question; unfortunately, whenever he was getting warm, the Irish secretly changed the Question, so that as he grew older and older Gladstone became angrier and angrier, and grander and grander, and was ultimately awarded the affectionate title of 'the G.P.O.' Gladstone was thus clearly a Good Man but a Bad Thing (or, alternatively, a Bad Man but a Good Thing).

Queen Victoria's Jamboree

Finally, all attempts (even by Gladstone and Disraeli) to amuse her, and to prevent her being good, having failed, the Queen held a Jamboree in Westminster Abbey and Crowned Heads and Oriental Patentees from all parts of the world came to acknowledge publicly the Good Queen's Victory over all her ministers and generals.

CHAPTER 58

The Boerwoer

THE last event in Queen Victoria's reign was the Borewore, or, more correctly, Boerwoer (Dutch), which was fought against a very tiresome Dutch tribe called the Bores, because they were left over from all previous wars.

The War was not a very successful one at first, and was quite unfair because the Boers could shoot much further than the English, and also because they were rather despicable in wearing veldt hats and using Pom-Pom bullets.

Numerous battles were fought against the Bore leaders (such as Bother, Kopje, and Stellenbosch) at Nek's Creek, Creek's Nek, Knock's Knee, etc., and much assistance was given to the British cause by Strathcoma's memorable horse (patriotically lent by Lord Strathcoma for the occasion) and by the C.I.D., who fought very bravely and were awarded a tremendous welcome on their return to London after the war.

Finally, the people at home took upon themselves the direction of the War and won it in a single night in London by a new and bracing method of warfare known as *Mafeking*. Thus the English were once more victorious.

The Barwar was obviously a Good Thing in the end because it was the cause of Boy Scouts and of their memorable Chief Scout, General Baden Powell (known affectionately as 'the B.O.P.'), and also because it gave rise to a number of very manly books, such as *40 Years Beating About The Bush*, *50 Years Before The Mast*, *60 Years Behind The Times*, etc.

Death of Queen Victoria

Meanwhile Queen Victoria had celebrated another Jamboree, called the Diamond Jamboree (on account of the discovery of Diamond mines at Camberley during the Borewore) and after dying of a surfeit of Jamborees, Jokes, Gladstone, etc., had been succeeded by her son, Edward VII.

CHAPTER 59

Wave of Inventions

THE reign of Queen Victoria was famous for the numerous discoveries and inventions which happened in it. One of the first of these was the brilliant theory of Mr Darwin propounded in his memorable works, *Tails of a Grandfather*, *The Manx Man*, *Our Mutual Friends*, etc. This was known as Elocution or the Origin of Speeches and was fiercely denounced in every pulpit.

Another memorable invention was called the Oxford Movement: this was a form of sinuflection which led men gradually in the direction of Rome; the movement was first made by Cardinal Newton at Oxford, and later, Peeble and Pusey Colleges were found there to commemorate his assistants. Many illustrated manuals and pamphlets were written by Cardinals Newton and Peeble, giving directions for the movement.

There was also in Queen Victoria's reign a famous inventor and poet called Oscar Wilde who wrote very well but behaved rather beardsley; he made himself memorable by inventing Art, Asceticism, etc., and was the leader of a set of disgusting old gentlemen called 'the naughty nineties'.

But most memorable of all were the McCanical inventions of the age, nearly all of which were kinds of Progress and invented by Scotsmen and Bad Things. Amongst these were Bicycles which caused Tricycles, coasting, bloomers, etc., and Roads (invented by Lord

Wrote very well
but . . .

Naughty nineties

Macadam and his son Lord Tarmac) for them to go along. Other inventions were Thermometers (invented by Lord Farqualqhounheit) which caused Temperatures, inflolqhouenza, etc.; Telegrams which caused betting, Bismark, etc.; Mackintoshes (invented by another Scottish nobleman whose name is now forgotten); and the memorable line invented by Mr Plimsoll (see diagram below).

Most of these inventions, however, were too numerous to be mentioned.

Mr Plimsoll's Invention.

CHAPTER 60

Edward VII: Almost a Monarch

EDWARD VII was quite old when he came to the throne, but this was only on account of Queen Victoria, and he was really a very active man and had many romantic occupations; for instance, he went betting and visited Paris and was sometimes late for dinner; in addition he was merry with actresses and kind to gypsies.

Besides all this Edward VII smoked cigars, was addicted to entente cordials, married a Sea-King's daughter, and invented appendicitis. Edward VII was thus a very Good King, besides being a Good Thing and *amused* and, in fact, almost a *Monarch*. He is also memorable because he preferred making peace instead of war.

CHAPTER 61

The Great War

KING EDWARD'S new policy of peace was very successful and culminated in the Great War to End War. This pacific and inevitable struggle was undertaken in the reign of His Good and memorable Majesty King George V and it was the cause of nowadays and the end of History.

Causes of the Great War

The Great War was between Germany and America and was thus fought in Belgium, one of the chief causes being the murder of the Austrian Duke of Sarajevo by a murderer in Servia.

There were many other Causes of the Great War, such as

1. German Governesses, a wave of whom penetrated Kensington in King Edward's reign and openly said that Germany ought to be top nation, and
2. The Kaiser, who sent a telegram consisting entirely of ems to one of the memorable Boerwar leaders.*

These are now agreed to have been causes of the War though at the time the newspapers (rather conceitedly) declared that it was caused by a *strip of paper*.

*And, during a subsequent crisis, a panther to Agaçiers (a brutal act and quite contrary to the Haig Convention).

The War

The War lasted three years or the duration, the Americans being 100% victorious. At the beginning the Russians rendered great assistance to the American cause by lending their memorable steam-roller and by passing silently through England one Sunday morning before breakfast with snow on their boots. The Americans were also assisted by the Australians (AZTECS) and some Canadians, and 51 Highlanders.

The Peace to End Peace

Though there were several battles in the War, none were so terrible or costly as the Peace which was signed afterwards in the ever-memorable Chamber of Horrors at Versailles, and which was caused by the only memorable American statesmen, President Wilson and Col. White House, who insisted on a lot of Points, including

1. that England should be allowed to pay for the War: this was a Good Thing because it strengthened British (and even American) credit;
2. that the world should be made safe for democracy, i.e. anyone except pillion-riders, pedestrians, foreigners, natives, capitalists, communists, Jews, riffs, R.A.F.S., gun-men, policemen, peasants, pheasants, Chinese, etc.;
3. that there should be a great many more countries: this was a Bad Thing as it was the cause of increased geography;
4. the Freedom of the Seas: this was a Good Thing as it did not apply to Britain or America (or Switzerland);
5. that the Kaiser should be hanged: this was a Good Thing

as it was abandoned, together with Mr Lloyd George, the Irish Question, etc.

CHAPTER 62

A Bad Thing

AMERICA was thus clearly top nation, and History came to a .

TEST PAPER V

Up to the End of History

1. Sketch vaguely, with some reference to the facts:
   (1) The Southsea Bubble, (2) The Ramillies Wig.
2. Would it have been a Good Thing if Wolfe had succeeded in writing Gray's Elegy instead of taking Quebec?
3. Analyse and distinguish between The Begums of Oudh. Would they have been deceived by the Banana Sahib?
4. 'An Army marches on its stomach' (Napoleon). Illustrate and examine.
5. Account (loudly) for the success of Marshal Ney as a leader of horse.
6a. 'What a city to boot!' Who said this, Wellington or Blücher or Flora McNightingown?
6b. Did anybody say 'I know that no one can save this country and that nobody else can'? If not, who did say it?
7. Ruminate fearlessly on (1) Lord Cardigan, (2) Clapham.

8. Do not attempt to remember what Mr Gladstone said in 1864 but account for the paramountcy of (1) Milk Puddings, (2) Bags, in his political career.

9. Comment *Quietly* on (*a*) Tariff Reform.

                                            (*b*) Mafeking Night.

                                            (*c*) The Western Front.

10. Refrain from commenting on The Albert Memorial, The September Massacres, The Dardanelles, The O.B.E., or any other subjects that you consider too numerous to mention. (The better the fewer.)

11. Write not more than two lines on The Career of Napoleon Buonaparte, *or* The Acquisition of our Indian Empire, *or* The Prime Ministers of England.

12. What price Glory?

N.B. – Do not on any account attempt to write on both sides of the paper at once.

MORE ABOUT PENGUINS
AND PELICANS

Penguinews, which appears every month, contains details of all the new books issued by Penguins as they are published. From time to time it is supplemented by *Penguins in Print*, which is a complete list of all titles available. (There are some five thousand of these.)

A specimen copy of *Penguinews* will be sent to you free on request. For a year's issues (including the complete lists) please send 50p if you live in the British Isles, or 75p if you live elsewhere. Just write to Dept EP, Penguin Books Ltd, Harmondsworth, Middlesex, enclosing a cheque or postal order, and your name will be added to the mailing list.

In the U.S.A.: For a complete list of books available from Penguin in the United States write to Dept CS, Penguin Books Inc., 7110 Ambassador Road, Baltimore, Maryland 21207.

In Canada: For a complete list of books available from Penguin in Canada write to Penguin Books Canada Ltd, 41 Steelcase Road West, Markham, Ontario.

THE PELICAN HISTORY OF ENGLAND

While each volume is complete in itself, the whole series, edited by J. E. Morpurgo, has been planned to provide an intelligent and consecutive guide to the development of English society in all its aspects. The nine volumes are:

1. ROMAN BRITAIN
   by Ian Richmond

2. THE BEGINNINGS OF ENGLISH SOCIETY
   (from the Anglo-Saxon Invasion)
   by Dorothy Whitelock

3. ENGLISH SOCIETY IN THE EARLY MIDDLE AGES
   by Doris Mary Stenton

4. ENGLAND IN THE LATE MIDDLE AGES
   by A. R. Myers

5. TUDOR ENGLAND
   by S. T. Bindoff

6. ENGLAND IN THE SEVENTEENTH CENTURY
   by Maurice Ashley

7. ENGLAND IN THE EIGHTEENTH CENTURY
   by J. H. Plumb

8. ENGLAND IN THE NINETEENTH CENTURY
   by David Thomson

9. ENGLAND IN THE TWENTIETH CENTURY
   by David Thomson

'As a portent in the broadening of popular culture the influence of this wonderful series has yet to receive full recognition and precise assessment. No venture could be more enterprising or show more confidence in the public's willingness to purchase thoughtful books. . . .' – *Listener*

RICHARD GORDON

'If you're feeling down in the dumps, this is just what you need' – *Daily Sketch*

DOCTOR IN CLOVER
DOCTOR IN THE HOUSE
DOCTOR IN LOVE
DOCTOR ON TOAST

Here are some press comments on Richard Gordon's books:

'Rich and racy humour and a shrewd and sympathetic understanding' – *Scotsman*

'His books are like an injection of elixir' – *Manchester Evening News*

'The golden formula . . . grafting Wodehouse on to the *Lancet*' – *New Statesman*

'One reads throughout with a gentle smile that breaks occasionally into a bark of laughter at some unexpected ribaldry or asperity' – *Sunday Times*

'Sheer unadulterated fun' – *Star*

NOT FOR SALE IN THE U.S.A.